COLEG MENAI
BANGOR, GWYNEDD LL57

MECHANICS AND SPORT PERFORMANCE

STOC DYNNWYD YMAITH
LLYFRGELL COLEG MENAI
WITHDRAWN LIBRARY STOCK

D0271175

COLEG MENAI
BANGOR, GWYNEDD LL57

MECHANICS AND SPORT PERFORMANCE

PETER WALDER

LLYFRGELL COLEG MENAI LIBRARY

SAF... ...FORDD FFRIDDOEDD ROAD SITE

BANGOR GWYNEDD LL57 2TP

FELTHAM PRESS

061774

Copyright, © P. Walder 1994

Published by Feltham Press 1994
Reprinted by Feltham Press 1995
Reprinted by Feltham Press 1996

All rights reserved. No part of this publication may be reproduced
or transmitted, in any form or by any means
without prior written permission of the Publishers.

ISBN   0   9520743   0   3

British Library Cataloguing-in-Publication Data.

A catalogue record for this book is available from the British Library.

To Colin and Siân

CONTENTS

1   DESCRIBING SPORT PERFORMANCE
LINEAR MOTION

1.1	Position, distance and displacement.	1
1.2	Speed and velocity.	3
	1.2.1 Average and instantaneous speeds/velocities.	5
	1.2.2 Direction.	6
1.3	Acceleration.	7
1.4	Vectors.	10
	1.4.1 Vector characteristics.	10
1.5	Resultant vectors.	11
	1.5.1 Construction technique.	11
	1.5.2 Numerical calculation.	12
1.6	Component vectors.	12
	1.6.1 Construction technique.	13
	1.6.2 Numerical calculation.	14
1.7	Graphical representation of linear motion quantities.	15
	1.7.1 Gradient/slope.	16
1.8	Numerical calculation of velocity and acceleration.	20

2   EXPLAINING SPORT PERFORMANCE
LINEAR MOTION *Part One*

2.1	Force.	25
2.3	Newton's First Law.	28
2.4	Newton's Second Law.	30
2.5	Newton's Third Law.	35
2.6	Net force.	37
	2.6.1 Forces in the take off phase of a vertical jump.	41
2.7	Impulse.	47
2.8	Forces and running.	52
2.9	Conservation of linear momentum.	58
2.10	Force and motion relationships.	60

3   EXPLAINING SPORT PERFORMANCE
LINEAR MOTION *Part Two*

3.1	Pressure.	62
3.2	Friction.	63
3.3	Projectiles.	65
	3.3.1 Projectile range.	69
3.4	Centre of gravity/centre of mass.	72
	3.4.1 Net force and centre of gravity/mass.	76

3.5	Stability.	76
3.6	Work, energy and power.	77

**4 DESCRIBING SPORT PERFORMANCE
ANGULAR MOTION**

4.1	Angular distance and angular displacement.	88
4.2	Angular speed and angular velocity.	90
4.3	Angular acceleration.	93

**5 EXPLAINING SPORT PERFORMANCE
ANGULAR MOTION**

5.1	Torque/moments.	96
	5.1.1 Net torque.	96
5.2	Levers.	97
	5.2.1 First class levers.	97
	5.2.2 Second class levers.	98
	5.2.3 Third class levers.	98
5.3	Rotation generation in sport performance.	99
	5.3.1 Support/contact situations.	99
	5.3.2 Non support situations.	102
5.4	Newton's First law - angular analogue.	103
5.5	Newton's Second law - angular analogue.	107
5.6	Newton's Third law - angular analogue.	109

**6 EXPLAINING SPORT PERFORMANCE
FLUID ENVIRONMENTS**

6.1	Fluid environments.	111
6.2	Interactions in an air environment.	112
	6.2.1 Velocity of flow and pressure differences.	112
	6.2.2 Factors affecting drag.	114
	6.2.3 Surface characteristics.	116
	6.2.4 Spin.	118
	6.2.5 Lift	119
6.3	Interactions in a water environment.	121
	6.3.1 Drag and lift.	121
	6.3.2 Buoyant force.	123

REFERENCES

Sports mechanics applications.	125

BIBLIOGRAPHY 127

APPENDIX

Units of measurement.	128

INDEX 129

ACKNOWLEDGMENTS

I would like to thank all those at Feltham Press for their efforts in ensuring that the book became a reality; especially Sam Denley for the creation of the artwork, and for his work in the production and design process. I would also like to thank Barrie Matthews for many constructive suggestions with regard to the text, Vicky Hart for technical advice on the diagrams, Ann Clegg for the many hours spent checking the manuscript, and all those who gave valuable time to trial some of the material in the classroom situation. Finally, special thanks to my wife for her support and encouragement given throughout the development of the book.

To Colin and Siân

PREFACE

The aim of this book is to provide a concise but comprehensive introduction to how performances in sport may be analysed using the principles of mechanics.

The principles of mechanics are those which aim to provide a means for the accurate description and explanation of motion and its changes. For performances in sport this has relevance to the techniques used to try and accomplish the aims of the sport, and the analysis may focus on the performer and/or associated sports equipment such as running shoes, balls, rackets, etc. Modifying and/or developing sports techniques or equipment using the principles of mechanics may provide the potential for improved performance.

The academic study of mechanical principles and their application in the analysis of performances in sport is called Sport Biomechanics or Sport Mechanics. The former of these two terms should ideally be reserved for investigations where the subject of study is specifically related to the mechanics of the performer *(a biological system)*. The second term has a wider meaning which can include the sports performer, sports equipment and sports implements as subjects of study. It is however necessary to recognise that in practice the term Sport Biomechanics is also commonly used in the wider sense in many textbooks and academic journals. Reference in this text to these two terms are made in this wider sense and no particular difference between the terms is meant to be implied.

Movement and changes in movement have always been an aspect of everyday human experience but only since Sir Isaac Newton have there been laws that allow the reliable explanation of motion and its changes. It is known today that even these laws are flawed at the level of explaining changes in motion at very small scales, such as the movement of atomic particles, and at very large scales such as the movement of the galaxies. However, for explanations of movement at the scale of everyday experience, including performances in sport, Newton's laws provide a good underpinning framework.

Newton's laws, and what they have to say about the relationship of the concept of force to changes in motion, are at the heart of the text. In order to investigate these relationships the information in the text has grouped movement into two main categories, namely linear and angular motion. It is essential to recognise from the outset that this grouping does not imply that a particular sport performance will fall into one or other of these categories. In the majority of cases a sport performance will be a complex mix of linear and angular motion but the groupings adopted by the text will assist an understanding of the mechanical principles.

In addition to the above grouping the material in the text has been further categorised according to two main approaches of analysis. In the first instance information has been grouped which is required for the accurate **description** of movement changes, and in the second instance information has been grouped which focusses on **explaining** changes in motion. These categories are reflected in the first five chapters of the book, namely:

Chapter 1
Describing Sport Performance - **Linear Motion;**

Chapter 2
Explaining Sport Performance - **Linear Motion** (Part 1);

Chapter 3
Explaining Sport Performance - **Linear Motion** (Part 2);

Chapter 4
Describing Sport Performance - **Angular Motion;**

Chapter 5
Explaining Sport Performance - **Angular** Motion;

(Note that the information within the category Explaining Sport Performance - Linear motion has been placed into two chapters to assist readability and not because there is an additional logical category).

Chapter 6
Explaining Sport Performance - **Fluid Enviroments;**

Sports Mechanics Applications of special interest are highlighted throughout in boxed sections.

Key Points of special importance are summarised at the end of each chapter.

Photocopiable Student Assignment Sheets, and Solutions, designed to help students work through this book, encourage self appraisal, and develop examination technique are available to accompany this volume.

x

1

DESCRIBING SPORT PERFORMANCE
LINEAR MOTION

OBJECTIVES:

To enable the reader to understand the following.

❖ The concepts of position, distance, displacement, speed, velocity and acceleration.

❖ The difference between vector and scalar quantities.

❖ How to manipulate vectors, to calculate vector resultants and vector components.

❖ How to construct and interpret graphical representations of linear motion.

❖ How to calculate linear velocity and acceleration using numerical techniques.

1.1 POSITION, DISTANCE AND DISPLACEMENT

Many questions which arise in mechanics are concerned with the accurate description of motion, whether it be of sportspersons, sports implements *(e.g. shot, discus)*, or sports equipment *(e.g. bobsleigh, tandem)*, etc.

The term **position** is used to identify the location of an object with reference to a datum line or point. If motion occurs so that the object takes up a new position, then the **distance** or **displacement** between the two positions may need to be identified. The distance in this case refers to the actual path taken in moving from the first position to the second, whilst the displacement refers to the shortest straight line route between the two positions. To illustrate this distinction consider the following example, and especially note the starting and finishing positions that are given.

A triathlon is to be held with the following elements:-

a) a swimming course 1.5 kilometres *(km)* in length in a straight line between two piers;

b) a cycling course of 8 laps of a 5 km road circuit, with the starting and finishing position at the same place;

c) a running course of one lap of a 10 km road circuit, with the start and finish separated by a 200 metre straight.

In swimming the first part of the race, the triathlete will have covered a 1.5 km distance, and at the same time experienced a displacement of 1.5 km: **Figure 1.1**.

Figure 1.1: *Displacement of triathlete during the swimming leg.*

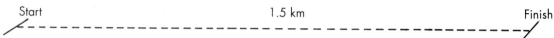

As the change of position was in a straight line, with no change of direction, then the two quantities are equivalent, except that the direction of the swim associated with the displacement should be specified. In this case the distance was 1.5 km, and the displacement was 1.5 km in an easterly direction.

On completion of the cycling component of the race, the triathlete will have covered a distance of 40 km, but will in fact have experienced a zero displacement, as the start and finish lines coincide: **Figure 1.2**. *(Note that any overshooting of the finish line by the cyclists is not included in this analysis.)*

Figure 1.2: *Displacement of triathlete during the cycling leg.*

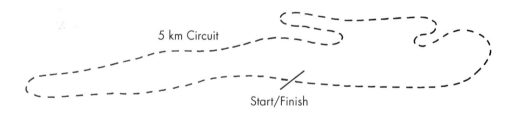

The final element of the triathlon will see the runners cover a distance of 10 km, but experience a displacement of 200 metres *(m)* in the direction of the start line to the finish line: **Figure 1.3**.

Figure 1.3: *Displacement of triathlete during the running leg.*

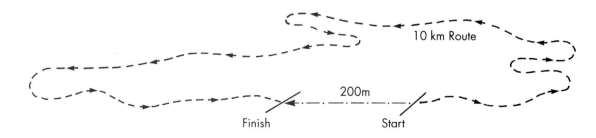

Although the distinction between these quantities may seem rather unnecessary, it is important when a thorough analysis of motion is required. In Chapter 2 it will be seen that a force is necessary to change an object's motion. The effect a force has on the object's motion is directly related to the directional component of an object's motion, as well as any changes in its speed. In order to describe fully a change in position experienced by an object, it is necessary to have a quantity which has a directional characteristic. Displacement has that directional characteristic.

When a measure such as displacement needs both its magnitude and its direction specified, then it is called a **vector** quantity. If only magnitude is required to specify the measure, as is the case with distance, then this is called a **scalar** quantity. The concept of vector quantities is particularly important in investigations of movements in sport, and the text will return to consider the concept of vectors later.

❖ Sports Mechanics Application

Simple position data have been used to identify different characteristics of running style. An investigation into the changing position of the top of the head during a running stride of two elite middle distance runners showed that one of the runners had a high degree of vertical motion. It was suggested that the runner may have been expending excessive energy in a direction which appeared to have no apparent benefit to the runner, that is vertically.

Simple position data were also used in the investigation to examine the stride length (distance between foot contact to the contact of the same foot) of the runner during a fatigued run. One of the runners displayed a gradually increasing stride length as the run developed, which is a typical pattern displayed by recreation runners. The other runner did not change stride length until the very last minute of the run. This suggested that this runner was able to maintain running style even during quite high levels of fatigue.

(Cavanagh 1985)

1.2 SPEED AND VELOCITY

In describing the changes of position that an object experiences, the question of how fast the change occurred is frequently important. From the above account it can be seen that a consideration of distance and displacement will be needed, as these describe changes in position. In addition, the time taken for the change in position to occur will also be a factor that needs to be taken into account.

Speed is one measure that can be used to quantify the rate of change of position, and in every day language it is this concept that is used to describe how fast an object is travelling, whether the object concerned is a car, a human, a bobsleigh, or an arrow, etc.

In biomechanical terms speed may be defined as follows:

$$\text{Speed} = \frac{\text{Distance covered}}{\text{Time taken}}$$

Many sports events would have the distance recorded in metres and the time in seconds, and therefore the units for speed in these cases are metres per second $(m \cdot s^{-1})$. Although these are the most common units, speed is also frequently described in units such as miles per hour, km per hour, or km per second, etc.

The question of 'how fast ?', when used in every day language, does not usually seek an answer which refers to the direction in which the object is travelling. However, this latter factor is often very important to the sport scientist, because as was noted earlier, changes in an object's motion, including direction, are directly related to the action of forces. Therefore the rate of change of position with reference to direction is calculated as **velocity**, where:

$$\text{Velocity} = \frac{\text{Displacement}}{\text{Time taken}}$$

Once again the magnitude of the calculated velocity is expressed in units of metres per second *(or equivalent)*, but in addition the direction should be specified.

Consider the example of the triathlon again. It is known that the winner covered the different elements of the race in the times shown in **Table 1.1**.

Table 1.1: *Winner's times for the different elements of a triathlon. (sf) = direction from start to finish*

Distance	Time	Displacement
1.5 km swim	30 min 30 secs	1.5 km *(sf)*
40.0 km cycle	90 min	0.0 km *(sf)*
10.0 km run	45 min	0.2 km *(sf)*

The average speeds and average velocities for the components of the triathlon would be as shown in **Table 1.2**.

Note that for the swimming component, the average speed, and magnitude of the average velocity, are the same, as the race took place in a straight line and did not involve a change of direction.

Table 1.2: *Average speeds and average velocities for the components of the triathlon.*

	Speed $(m \cdot s^{-1})$	Velocity $(m \cdot s^{-1})$ (*Average values*)
Swim	0.82	0.82 in the direction of start to finish.
Cycle	7.41	0.00
Run	3.70	0.07 in the direction of start to finish.

The important point of the example is that there is a difference between speed and velocity. The usefulness of using velocity as a way of describing motion may not be apparent at this stage. However, once again, the key to the significance of this difference is the relationship between force and motion, and this is explored further in Chapter 2.

1.2.1 AVERAGE AND INSTANTANEOUS SPEEDS/VELOCITIES

It is essential to note that the above data relate to the **average speed** and the **average velocity** that the triathletes achieved in the three components of the race. Considering what would have actually happened during the race, it may be noted that the athlete's speed/velocity would have been constantly fluctuating. However, for these changes to be identified, a great deal more information would need to be known. In fact changes in position over a very short time period *(or alternatively time taken for known small changes of position)* would need to be available. When such information is available, then the speeds or velocities may be considered to be those acting at an instant, and are described therefore as **instantaneous speed** and **instantaneous velocity.**

Some further development of these ideas will be undertaken later, but it is worth noting that in sport mechanics, hi-speed cine film is frequently used as the basis for analysing movement in sport. Typically, frame rates of between 50 to 200 frames per second are used, and therefore when changes in position are recorded, the time interval may be as small as 0.005 of a second. Speed/velocity calculations conducted on such data could be considered as average values. That is, the average for the change in position recorded for two adjacent frames of film. In practice such a calculation would frequently be regarded as producing a value which was a good approximation to the instantaneous value as the time interval is so small.

❖ *Sports Mechanics Application*

Coaches and performers who take part in sports which involve throwing or bowling a ball/implement are often interested in finding out how fast the ball/implement is travelling when it is released. Using high speed film, sport scientists can get a good estimate of the release speed. One such investigation has looked at a number of top class bowlers, and the four best speeds are shown below:

G. Dilley	*39.59 m·s-1*
G. Small	*38.47 m·s-1*
A. Donald	*38.37 m·s-1*
R. Patterson	*36.15 m·s-1*

Once the speeds have been worked out the scientist will then wish to ask questions which try to work out why one particular performer is better than another. This will involve first describing the actual movement patterns of the performer in detail and then looking at the causes of these movement patterns. The end of the process may lead to the performer changing his/her techniques; adopting different training methods to develop more strength, flexibility or stamina; or a combination of these and other factors. In the case of the cricket investigation it was noted that the less talented cricketers did not brace their front leg so well and had slower upper arm angular velocities. These factors may contribute to the differences observed between the performances of elite and club cricketers.

(Burden and Bartlett 1989).

1.2.2 DIRECTION

The importance of direction when describing motion has already been mentioned. The following examples from sport situations provide a convenient link to a better understanding of the significance of direction. The examples involve movement in a straight line, but changes in direction along that line are also involved.

A vertical jump at a rugby line out, a basketball tip off, a volleyball block, a shuttle run during a training session, a swimmer swimming lengths of a pool; all of these display movement which can be considered to take place in a straight line, and involve a change in direction along that line. Consider the shuttle run example. The runner starts from rest and then gains forward motion in the direction of the end of the first length of the shuttle. At the end of the first length the runner comes momentarily to rest, changes direction, and then returns to the starting position, where s/he comes to rest. An investigation of the changes in speed might show an increase from 0 m·s^{-1} to 5 m·s^{-1}, and then a return at the end of the first length to 0 m·s^{-1}. The speed might then increase once more to 5 m·s^{-1} before returning to 0 m·s^{-1} at the end of the shuttle run. Note that in this description the values of speed do not in themselves communicate anything about the direction of the run.

The same analysis using velocity to describe the motion would have to specify the direction. For events displaying these movement characteristics this can be done by indicating direction via the use of + and – signs. If the initial direction of the shuttle run was assumed to be the positive direction, then the velocity of the runner at the same points in the shuttle as described above would be 0 m·s^{-1}, $+5 \text{ m·s}^{-1}$, 0 m·s^{-1}, -5 m·s^{-1} and 0 m·s^{-1}.

Although the number of sport activities that can be directly modelled in this way is limited *, the kind of analysis just undertaken does give an indication of how a velocity value can contain a greater amount of information than a speed value. It also emphasises the very important point that a change in velocity occurs when there is a change in the magnitude of speed and/or direction. This last point leads to a consideration of another quantity used to describe linear motion and that is acceleration.

(A later passage (section 1.6) on component vectors introduces analysis ideas which allow the complete range of sports events to be fully described using vector principles)

1.3 ACCELERATION

In the same way that velocity represents the rate of change of position with respect to direction, so **acceleration** represents the rate of change of velocity and thus can be defined as:

$$\text{Acceleration} = \frac{\text{Change in velocity}}{\text{Time taken}}$$

The units for acceleration are metres per second per second *(m·s^{-2})*. This can at first sight appear to be a strange unit, but examination of the above formula will show that a velocity value which has a unit of metres per second, is being divided by time which has a unit of seconds.

Acceleration is derived from velocity, and it too is a vector quantity and therefore has the attributes of magnitude and direction. An acceleration will therefore be experienced when there is:

a) a change in the magnitude of the velocity *(ie speed)*; or

b) a change in direction; or

c) a change in both magnitude and direction.

In the same way that average and instantaneous values may be calculated for velocity, so acceleration values may also be considered as average or instantaneous. If instantaneous velocity values are known then acceleration may be defined as follows:

$$\bar{a} = \frac{v_f - v_i}{t}$$

where:

$\bar{a}$ = average acceleration;

v_f = final velocity;

v_i = initial velocity;

t = time interval.

Consider first the situation of a 100 m race where there is no change of direction. Assume that the velocity of the runner in the direction of the start to finish line has been recorded at 20 m intervals to be as shown in **Table 1.3**.

Table 1.3: *Instantaneous velocity of the runner recorded at 20 m intervals.*

metres (*m*)	0	20	40	60	80	100
v (*m·s⁻¹*)	0.0	8.5	11.1	11.5	11.5	9.5
t (*s*)	0.0	2.9	5.6	7.6	9.4	11.4

From **Table 1.3** it can be seen that the change in velocity in the first 20 m interval was 8.5 m·s⁻¹, and the time taken for this change was 2.9 s. Therefore using the formula, change in velocity divided by time, the average acceleration over the first 20 m was 2.93 m·s⁻². Repeating the calculation for the other intervals gives the result shown in **Table 1.4**.

Table 1.4: *Average acceleration over 20 m intervals of 100 m.*

d (*m*)	0	20	40	60	80	100
$\bar{a}$ (*m·s⁻²*)		2.93	0.96	0.20	0.00	−1.00

Looking at **Table 1.4** it may be noted that in this example a positive acceleration is associated with the runner getting faster, and a negative acceleration with the runner slowing down *(decelerating)*. However, there are a number of cautionary points that must be made with regard to this interpretation.

a) Positive and negative accelerations can only be associated with speeding up and slowing down when the movement being considered is in a straight line with no change of direction.

b) The positive and negative accelerations do **not** indicate the direction in which the runner is moving.

c) The term deceleration should not automatically be equated with negative acceleration as it is possible to be experiencing a negative acceleration and to be getting faster.

❖ *Sports Mechanics Application*

Sport scientists in Germany use a special indoor running track to assess their best sprinters. The track has timing devices positioned every 10 m which are automatically triggered as the runner passes. The times are then used in association with the known position data to calculate the velocity and acceleration for each 10 m section of the track. Coaches then use this information to try and assess the performance of the sprinters in terms of questions such as the following.

Where in the race was the maximum speed attained ?

What were the average accelerations in each 10 m section ?

The results from the analysis can then be used to inform the runners and their coaches of the strengths and weaknesses of the performance.

Consider now a second example which emphasises the points made above. In the shuttle run example referred to earlier, although the motion took place in a straight line, there was a change of direction. Assume that the following instantaneous velocity data, shown in **Table 1.5**, have been taken from a shuttle run over two lengths of a 30 m course, with a starting and finishing velocity of 0 m·s^{-1}. The positive direction is assumed to be that of the first leg of the shuttle.

Table 1.5: *Instantaneous velocity data from a shuttle run.*

metres (m)	0.0	10.0	20.0	30.0	40.0	50.0	60.0
v $(m·s^{-1})$	0.0	3.6	7.0	0.0	−3.8	−6.8	0.0
t (s)	0.0	2.0	3.4	5.0	7.0	8.6	10.5
$\bar{a}$ $(m·s^{-2})$		1.8	2.4	−4.4	−1.9	−1.9	3.6

During the first two 10 m intervals the runner accelerates from rest and experiences a positive acceleration. For the last 10 m of the first leg , when the runner is preparing to change direction, the average acceleration experienced is negative. During the interval immediately after changing direction the runner is speeding up, but note that the acceleration experienced is in fact negative. This is also the case for the interval between 40 m - 50 m. In the final phase of the shuttle, when the runner is coming to rest, the average acceleration experienced by the runner is positive.

The accelerations outlined above may seem rather puzzling, but careful application of the formula will confirm the results. For a complete understanding of the patterns of acceleration displayed it is necessary to explore further the concept of vectors, and to introduce the concept of force. A section on vectors follows.

1.4 VECTORS

It has already been noted that measures such as displacement, velocity and acceleration are described by their magnitude and direction , and therefore are **vector** quantities, *(those measures that only specify magnitude, eg distance and speed, are called scalar quantities.)* The concept of vectors is important to an understanding of many movements in sport, but this text will only deal briefly with some basic concepts.

1.4.1 VECTOR CHARACTERISTICS

Arrows are used to represent vector quantities, the length of the arrow may be considered to be proportional to the magnitude of the vector quantity, and the alignment and direction of the arrow head to indicate the direction. The velocity of a cricket ball at the moment of release would therefore be represented as in **Figure 1.4**.

It should be noted that if the ball were to be released at twice the speed and in the same direction, the arrow in the diagram would be twice as long.

Frequently in mechanics two *(or more)* vector quantities need to be combined. The outcome of the combination procedure is itself a vector, and this vector is termed a **resultant**. There are some simple construction procedures that can be used to obtain the resultant. Consider **Figure 1.5**, this shows the horizontal velocity of a golf ball as it leaves the ground, having been chipped towards the green on a day when there is no wind.

Figure 1.4: *Velocity of cricket ball at the moment of release.*

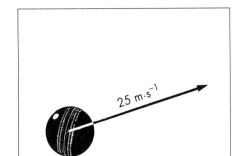

Figure 1.5: *Vector representing the horizontal velocity of a golf ball as it is chipped towards the green on a wind free day, as viewed from above.*

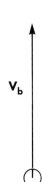

V_b velocity acquired by the ball as a result of the actions of the golfer

On a day when there is a cross wind the golfer's aim will have to be adjusted, because the wind will impart a velocity to the arrow in a sideways direction. **Figure 1.6** shows the two velocity vectors and also the resultant velocity. It should be noted that the diagram shows the velocity at one particular instant, and that the direction of the golf ball will be constantly changing during its flight, assuming that the cross wind is present.

Figure 1.6: *Vectors representing the horizontal velocities of a golf ball, cross wind, and the associated resultant. (In the above analysis no account has been taken of any aerodynamic influences that might have resulted from spin imparted to the ball. Consideration is given to the effects of spin in Chapter 6 (section 6.2.4).*

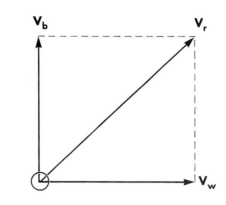

V_b velocity acquired by the ball as a result of the actions of the golfer
V_w velocity acquired by the ball as a result of the wind.
V_r resultant velocity of the ball at the instant shown.

1.5 RESULTANT VECTORS

The resultant of two vectors may be calculated using both construction and numerical techniques. Some examples of these techniques are shown in the following sections.

Figure 1.7: *R is the resultant vector of vectors C_1 and C_2*

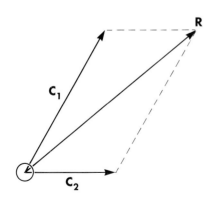

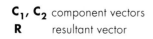

C_1, C_2 component vectors
R resultant vector

1.5.1 CONSTRUCTION TECHNIQUE

The resultant in **Figure 1.7** has been calculated using the parallelogram method. The stages in construction are as follows:

a) Draw the initial two vectors from a common point with arrows accurately representing the magnitudes and direction of the vectors.

b) The missing two sides of a parallelogram are constructed, and the diagonal of this parallelogram, which shares the common point of the other two vectors, will represent the resultant.

It may be noted that if the vectors are acting at right angles to one another, then the parallelogram will be a rectangle. Therefore if the magnitude of the two original vectors is known, the magnitude of the resultant can be calculated by using Pythagoras's theorem. The direction can be determined by using simple trigonometry to work out the angle. An example of this method is shown in the next section. *(Numeric methods also exist for vectors not at right angles, but these will not be covered in this text).*

1.5.2 NUMERICAL CALCULATION

According to Pythagoras's theorem the square built on the hypotenuse will have an area equal to the sum of the squares built on the other two sides of a right angled triangle. In this example it therefore follows that:

$$R^2 = (10 \text{ m·s}^{-1})^2 + (8 \text{ m·s}^{-1})^2$$

$$R^2 = 100 + 64$$

$$R^2 = 164$$

$$R = \sqrt{164}$$

The magnitude of the resultant is therefore: $R = 12.81$ m·s^{-1}.

The angle *(direction)* of the vector can be calculated using basic trigonometry. For the above set of data it therefore follows that:

$$\text{Tan } \theta = \frac{8}{10} = 0.8$$

$$\theta = \text{Tan}^{-1} 0.8$$

The angle of the resultant to the horizontal is therefore:

$$\theta = 38.66°$$

In an earlier example it was noted that a golf ball's direction will be affected by the effects of a cross wind. The above analysis indicates that the golfer must not aim directly at the pin, but where there is a left to right cross wind, s/he must start the ball off to the left of the pin so that the wind brings the ball back on line. The precise direction in which the ball must be set off will depend on the strength with which the ball is hit and the strength of the cross wind. It is part of the skill of being a good golfer that enables correct judgements to be made in situations such as these.

1.6 COMPONENT VECTORS

Just as vectors can be combined to find a resultant, the reverse procedure can be applied, so that a single vector may be split up into two components. Usually the components of most interest are those that are perpendicular *(that is at right angles)* to one another. The process of splitting a vector up is called **resolving a vector into its components**.

Consider the example of a long jumper who has a take off velocity as represented in **Figure 1.8**.

The horizontal and vertical component velocities of the jumper may be calculated as follows.

An arrow is drawn whose length is proportional to the speed of the jumper *(e.g. 1 cm represents 1 m·s^{-1})*, and whose alignment represents the direction.

Figure 1.8: *Long jumper with a take off velocity of 8 m·s⁻¹ at an angle of 20°*

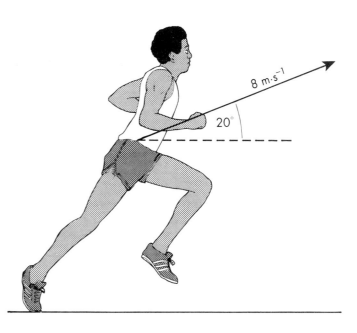

A right angled triangle is constructed, on the basis that the given arrow is the hypotenuse, and that the horizontal and vertical sides are drawn parallel to the true horizontal and vertical.

The lengths of the horizontal and vertical sides of the constructed triangle, represent the magnitude of the horizontal and vertical velocities, and can therefore be measured to get the actual values.

If the angle of the take off velocity vector is known, then the horizontal and vertical component velocities can be calculated using simple trigonometry. Both of these methods are illustrated in the following section.

1.6.1 CONSTRUCTION TECHNIQUE

a) The line representing the vector is drawn so that it is scaled to the magnitude it represents, and is at the correct angle: **Figure 1.9**.

Figure 1.9: *Line representing the vector drawn so that it is scaled to the magnitude it represents, and at the correct angle.*

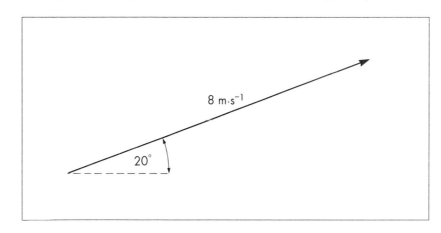

b) Two additional lines are drawn, one from the point of application of the vector, and one from the arrow head. They intersect at 90° and so form a right angled triangle in association with the original vector. These two new constructed lines represent the horizontal and vertical components of the original vector: **Figure 1.10**

Figure 1.10: *Two additional lines drawn, one from the point of application of the vector, and one from the arrow head intersecting at 90° to form a right angled triangle in association with the original vector. The two new constructed lines represent the horizontal and vertical components of the original vector.*

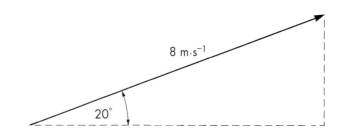

c) The lengths of the two new lines are measured, and when scaled give the magnitudes of the horizontal and vertical velocity components: **Figure 1.11**.

Figure 1.11: *The lengths of the two new lines measured and scaled to give the magnitudes of the horizontal and vertical velocity components.*

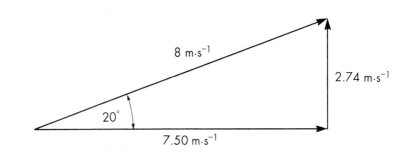

1.6.2 NUMERICAL CALCULATION

a) A right angled triangle is drawn where the hypotenuse represents the original vector, and the other two sides the horizontal and vertical components. Drawing the diagram to scale is not critical: **Figure 1.12**.

Figure 1.12: *A right angled triangle drawn where the hypotenuse represents the original vector, and the other two sides the horizontal and vertical components.*

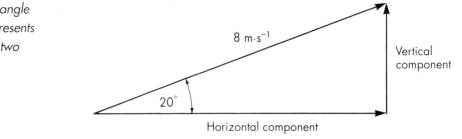

b) Trigonometry is used to calculate the lengths of the horizontal and vertical sides of the triangle, shown as follows.

Horizontal Component

$$\text{Cos } 20° = \frac{X}{8}$$

$$X = 8 \times \text{Cos } 20°$$

$$X = 8 \text{ m·s}^{-1} \times 0.94$$

$$X = 7.52 \text{ m·s}^{-1}$$

Vertical Component

$$\text{Sin } 20° = \frac{Y}{8}$$

$$Y = 8 \text{ m·s}^{-1} \times \text{Sin } 20°$$

$$Y = 8 \text{ m·s}^{-1} \times 0.34$$

$$Y = 2.72 \text{ m·s}^{-1}$$

❖ *Sports Mechanics Application*

An investigation by Hay et al (1986) looked at the way in which the horizontal and vertical velocity of twelve elite long jumpers changed during the last phase of the run up, and during the take off itself. The results showed that the long jumpers had typical horizontal velocities of about 10 m·s^{-1} as they started the take off, and during the take off lost between 10–20% of this velocity. Their vertical velocity as they started the take off step was negative (between - 0.2 m·s^{-1} and - 1.6 m·s^{-1}) so they were travelling in a downwards direction. During the take off the jumpers gained approximately 4 m·s-1 of vertical velocity. For the jumpers investigated, greater loss in horizontal velocity was associated with greater gains in vertical velocity. The ratio of horizontal velocity to vertical velocity of the jumpers approximated to 3 : 1 and the angles of take off ranged between 18.7°–22.8°. The experiment included world class jumpers (e.g. Carl Lewis, Mike Conley) and therefore may help to provide 'benchmark' information, against which other jumper's performances can be compared.

1.7 GRAPHIC REPRESENTATION OF LINEAR MOTION QUANTITIES

Graphs can provide a useful aid to understanding the characteristics of motion. Consider the data in **Table 1.6**, which show the two kilometre times for a 10 km road race.

Table 1.6 *Two - kilometre times for a 10 km race.*

Distance (km)	2	4	6	8	10
Time (min)	7	14	21	28	35

The graph for this data would look like the one shown in **Figure 1.13**.

Figure 1.13: *Graph of distance versus time for a 10 km road race.*

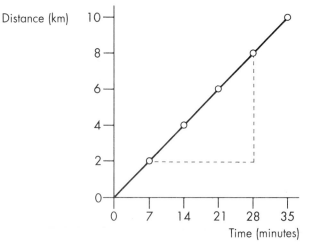

Because the runner covers the same distance per unit of time, s/he is travelling at a constant speed. This speed information can be observed on the graph by looking at the slope *(or gradient)* of the line. An example of how the gradient of a line is calculated will show why the slope of the graph provides speed information.

1.7.1 GRADIENT/SLOPE

The gradient or slope of a line is defined as being equal to the change in value of the variable represented on the vertical axis *(Y)* divided by the corresponding change in the value represented on the horizontal axis *(X)*.

$$\text{Gradient} = \frac{\text{Change in Y}}{\text{Change in X}}$$

This is best observed if a right angled triangle is constructed on the

Figure 1.14: *Distance versus time graph showing a relatively steep slope and therefore a relatively high speed.*

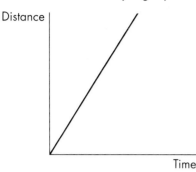

Figure 1.15: *Distance versus time graph showing a relatively shallow slope and therefore a relatively low speed.*

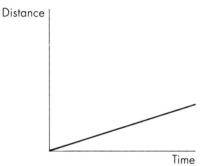

Figure 1.16: *Speed versus time graph for constant speed situations.*

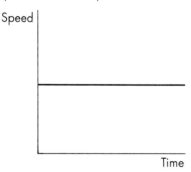

Figure 1.17: *Distance versus time graph for 100 m sprint.*

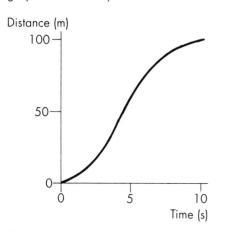

line as indicated in **Figure 1.13** The length of the vertical side of the triangle represents the change of the variable on the vertical axis. The horizontal side of the triangle represents the change in variable represented on the horizontal axis.

In this particular case, the calculation will involve dividing a distance value by a time value, and therefore the outcome of this division will be a speed value. In making this interpretation, there are two points that need to be made.

a) In constructing the right angled triangles it does not make any difference where on the line the construction takes place, as the slope of a straight line does not change. Because of this, it often makes sense to choose a construction so that the horizontal side of the triangle is matched up with the unit divisions on the horizontal axis.

b) For the same event, a line with a steep slope will represent a relatively high speed, and a graph with a shallow slope a relatively low speed. This is shown in **Figures 1.14 and 1.15**.

If the example is taken a stage further by taking the gradient at a number of points, the information that is obtained could be used to plot a speed versus time graph. In this particular case the graph would look like the one shown in **Figure 1.16**.

In real situations in sport, constant speed rarely occurs. Even for the previous example, a few moments thought would indicate that the runner must have changed his/her speed at the start of the race *(that is the athlete must have started from a stationary position)*, but the nature of the data in the example did not allow these changes to be represented.

Consider a 100 m race which takes place on a straight track with the runners moving in a direction from the start line to the finish line. A distance versus time graph for such an event might look like the one in **Figure 1.17**.

Unlike the previous example, it is immediately apparent (by observing the gradient of the curve), that the speed of the runner is not constant. The average speed for the whole race could be calculated by simply considering the time taken to cover the 100 m. That is the average speed equals $\frac{100 \text{ m}}{\text{time}}$. However the graph provides more information than this.

For example, an average speed for the first two seconds could be calculated by looking at the graph, noting the distance covered during the first two seconds, and doing the simple calculation of dividing the distance by time.

This approach essentially assumes that it is reasonable to model the curve as a straight line. Observation of the graph in **Figure 1.18** shows that at this part of the curve this assumption is not a particularly good one, but for other time intervals such as 4.0–5.0 seconds, a straight line would fit closely to the actual shape of the trace.

Figure 1.18: *Distance versus time graph for 100 m sprint.*

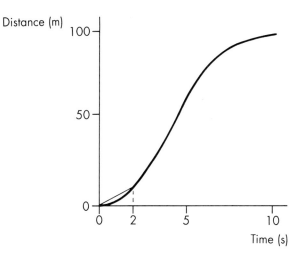

Similar calculations could be undertaken for other time intervals, and so a series of average speed values calculated. These values could then be plotted against time to produce a speed versus time graph. This procedure, however, does not utilise all the information available from the graph.

Consider the time interval between 7.0-8.0 seconds. As has already been demonstrated, an average speed for this time interval could be calculated. However, a one second period is still a relatively large period of time, and there is no reason why the time interval should not be 7.0-7.5 or 7.0-7.25 or 7.0-7.125 seconds or even smaller. By considering ever smaller time intervals, the value of speed obtained would be approaching that of instantaneous speed at 7.0 seconds. If this idea is applied to the graph then a line can be drawn which notionally passes through two infinitely close points. This line is called a tangent, and **Figure 1.19** shows how this would look for the example data.

The gradient of the tangent can be calculated by constructing a right-angled triangle, and dividing the distance represented on the vertical side by the time represented on the horizontal side. The value obtained will be the instantaneous speed at 7.0 seconds.

By repeating the process at a number of points, a series of instantaneous speeds could be calculated, and a speed versus time graph constructed.

Figure 1.19: *Distance versus time graph for 100 m sprint. (Note that it does not matter where on the tangent the triangle is constructed, therefore, it is often convenient to construct the horizontal side of the triangle to correspond to a regular time interval e.g., 1 or 2 seconds (s)).*

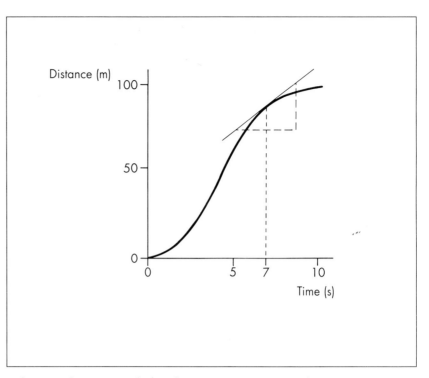

The speed-time graph for the 100 metre race is shown in **Figure 1.20**.

Figure 1.20: *Speed versus time graph for 100 m race.*

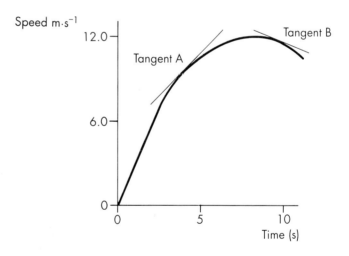

In the same way that the gradient of a distance time graph revealed useful information, so the gradient or slope of a speed versus time graph is also informative.

In this case, the gradient gives information about the acceleration of the athlete. Note, that the information gained from the gradient of a speed versus time graph, is in fact the magnitude of the acceleration associated with changes in speed only.

For events where a velocity-time graph is legitimately drawn, then the gradient reveals information about the magnitude and direction of the acceleration.

Identical procedures to those used to calculate the gradient of a distance versus time graph may be used to work out the gradient *(and thus acceleration)* of a speed-time graph. In the case of the 100 m data, the tangents that can be drawn may give both positive and negative values, and these can legitimately *(for this event)* be interpreted as positive and negative accelerations. In **Figure 1.20** tangent 'A' has a positive slope and therefore represents a positive acceleration, and tangent 'B' has a negative slope and therefore represents a negative acceleration.

For events such as the long jump which cannot be modelled as taking place along a straight line a complete graphical description of the motion would require both vertical and horizontal motion to be graphed.

1.8 NUMERICAL CALCULATION OF VELOCITY & ACCELERATION

To derive speed/velocity and acceleration values purely on the basis of construction and graphical techniques is not only time consuming, but also prone to inaccuracy in the drawing of the graph, and the positioning of the tangent.

Numerical techniques can be used to obtain the required velocity and acceleration values, however, these have their own problems, as the position data from which other quantities are derived have to be very accurate. Small errors in position data are greatly magnified by the numerical processes, so care has to be taken when using numerical procedures.

The data in **Table 1.7** represent the motion of someone performing a vertical jump. Movement of a point at the centre of the body, *(see discussion of centre of gravity and centre of mass later ;section 3.4))*, is considered to represent the movement of the body as a whole. The jump may be considered to take place along a completely vertical line of action, and therefore displacement and velocity measures may be usefully used to describe the motion. **Table 1.7** shows the steps needed to calculate velocity data using straight forward numerical techniques.

Table 1.7: *Data representing the motion of a vertical jump.*

COL 1	COL 2	COL 3	COL 4	COL 5
T (s)	Pos (cm)	Dis (cm)	Dis (m)	Vel (m·s⁻¹)
0.00	102.0			
		0.0	0.000	0.00
0.05	102.0			
		0.0	0.000	0.00
0.10	102.0			
		– 1.0	– 0.010	– 0.20
0.15	101.0			
		– 1.0	– 0.010	– 0.20
0.20	100.0			
		– 2.0	– 0.020	– 0.40
0.25	98.0			
		– 4.0	– 0.040	– 0.80
0.30	94.0			
		– 6.0	– 0.060	– 1.20
0.35	88.0			
		– 6.0	– 0.060	– 1.20
0.40	82.0			
		– 4.0	– 0.040	– 0.80
0.45	78.0			
		– 3.5	– 0.035	– 0.70
0.50	74.5			
		– 2.0	– 0.020	– 0.40
0.55	72.5			
		0.0	0.000	0.00
0.60	72.5			
		3.0	0.030	0.60
0.65	75.5			
		6.0	0.060	1.20
0.70	81.5			
		11.0	0.110	2.20
0.75	92.5			
		13.0	0.130	2.60
0.80	105.5			
		12.0	0.120	2.40
0.85	117.5			

The values in **Table 1.7** have been calculated in the following stages.

First the displacement is calculated by finding the change in position *(in cm)* over successive time intervals, and this value *(COL 3)* is then converted to metre units *(COL 4)*. The displacement value is then divided by the time interval over which the change in position took place to give the velocity *(COL 5)*. The position and velocity values can then be plotted on a graph to give an overall representation of the movement. This is shown in **Figures 1.21** and **1.22**.

Figure 1.21: *Graph showing the changes in position during the take off phase of a vertical jump. The trace shows the position of the jumper's centre of gravity.*

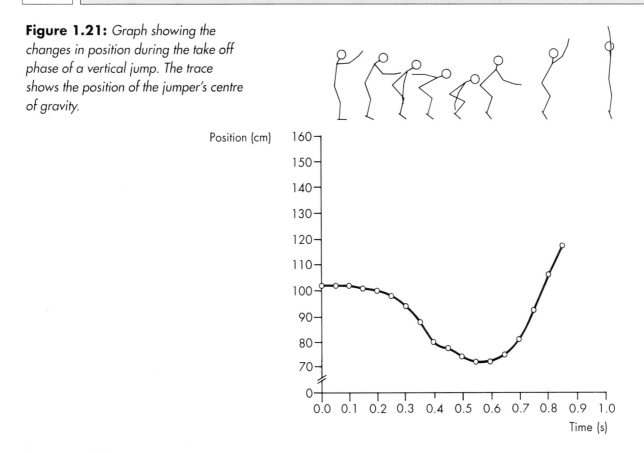

Figure 1.22: *Graph showing vertical velocity versus time trace for the take off phase of a vertical jump.*

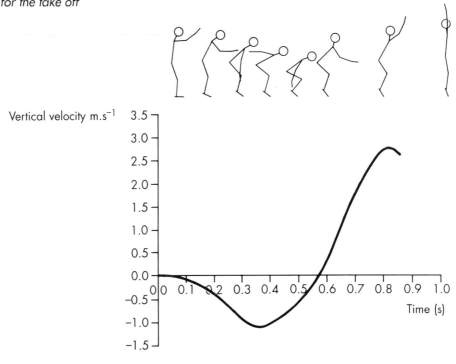

The formula for acceleration was given earlier as:

$$\bar{a} = \frac{\text{change in velocity}}{\text{time taken}}$$

By extending the numerical process explained above it is possible to calculate the acceleration.

The key stages in the extended procedure are as follows.

a) Find the difference between the velocity values that have been calculated in Col 5.

b) Divide the difference values by time *(in this case 0.05 s)*

This process gives a series of average acceleration values which can be plotted as an acceleration versus time graph.

It should be noted that using a difference procedure for a second time on a set of data will tend to give results which show considerable variations from what might be expected. For this reason interpreting acceleration graphs should be done carefully.

❖ *Sports Mechanics Application*

Analysis of vertical and horizontal component velocities is frequently used by sport biomechanicians when describing a movement in detail.

One good example of this is shown in a study by Miller (1986), who looked at the vertical and horizontal velocity components of elite spring board divers performing a variety of dives. In general divers need to have a relatively large vertical velocity at take off in order to give them sufficient time in the air to complete their move, whilst at the same time retaining a relatively low horizontal velocity which will keep their travel away from the board down to a minimum, but still large enough so that they do not collide with the board on the downward phase of their flight.

Miller's investigation showed that for the same dive, male divers had higher vertical velocities and lower horizontal velocities than female divers. Although the male divers had a lower horizontal velocity than the female divers they were in the air for longer before reaching the level of the board so had enough time to travel far enough away from the board to avoid collision. (See Chapter 3 (section 3.3) on projectiles for more information).

SUMMARY

At this point in the text the reader has been introduced to the following key ideas.

❖ Description of motion using position, distance and displacement measures.

❖ Description of motion changes using velocity and acceleration.

❖ The significance of direction as an element in motion description.

❖ The significance of average and instantaneous measures.

❖ The difference between scalar and vector quantities.

❖ The calculation of resultant vectors using construction and numerical techniques.

❖ The calculation of component vectors using construction and numerical techniques.

❖ The graphical representation of motion using distance versus time graph.

❖ The graphical representation of motion using speed *(velocity)* versus time graph.

❖ The significance of the gradient of distance versus time, and speed versus time graphs.

❖ Numerical techniques for calculating velocity.

❖ Numerical techniques for calculating acceleration.

EXPLAINING SPORT PERFORMANCE

LINEAR MOTION
Part One

OBJECTIVES:

To enable the reader to understand the following.

❖ Basic ideas associated with the concept of force.

❖ The principles of Newton's Law of Gravitation.

❖ The principles of Newton's First Law of Motion.

❖ The principles of Newton's Second Law of Motion.

❖ The principles of Newton's Third Law of Motion.

❖ The concept of impulse.

❖ Principle of conservation of momentum.

2.1 FORCE

Forces arise whenever objects interact with each other. This interaction may be one where the relationship between the objects is one of contact or non-contact. From this simple description it can be seen that forces are present at all times, and an understanding of force is fundamental to an understanding of motion. The essential significance of force may be summarised as follows.

A net force is required to change the state of motion of an object. Such a change occurs when there is:

a) an increase in the speed of the object;

b) a decrease in the speed of the object;

c) a change in direction of the object independent of, or in association with, the changes in speed.

Note that these three points can be summarised as a 'change of velocity'.

In order to examine this change in more detail it is necessary to consider the nature of the interactions between objects and the associated forces.

Forces can be classified in a number of ways but the classification into contact and non-contact *(Enoka 1988)* is the one adopted here. Under this classification forces may be considered to be grouped as follows.

Non contact	Contact
Gravity	'Ground' reaction forces.
	Joint reaction forces.
	Muscle forces.
	Fluid forces.
	Elastic forces.

Of the forces identified above, those considered in this section are gravity and ground reaction forces. Whilst this means an analysis of motion may be incomplete, the use of these two categories will enable a good understanding of many sports movements to be achieved.

Before proceeding to a further explanation of these forces, it is necessary to indicate that the examples used in this section to support the explanation of force, involve situations where forces should be considered to be external to the 'system of interest'.

Whether a force is regarded as 'external' or 'internal' entirely depends on the object or system that is the focus of interest. For example if the 'object' or system of interest is the sports performer *(that is the whole body)*, then forces such as muscle forces and joint forces which arise within the body are 'internal', and forces such as gravity and ground reaction forces are 'external'.

However, in another investigation it might be appropriate to consider an individual segment of the body to be the 'system of interest'. In such a case, muscle forces and joint forces *(as well as gravity and ground reaction forces)* will be considered to be 'external' to the system

Although this might seem a rather complicated set of terms, it is essential to note that it is only those forces that are defined as 'external' to the system of interest that can cause a net change in the state of motion of that system.

2.2 GRAVITY

For the purpose of this text it is reasonable to consider gravity as the only non-contact force that needs to be identified. Sir Isaac Newton explained gravitational interaction in what is now known as Newton's Law of Gravitation which can be defined as follows.

All particles attract one another with a force proportional to the product of their masses, and inversely proportional to the square of the distance between them.

This can be expressed as:

$$F \quad = \quad G \times \left(\frac{m_1 \times m_2}{d^2} \right)$$

where:

F =   gravitational force;
m_1 =   mass of particle one;
m_2 =   mass of particle two;
d =   distance between particles;
G =   constant.

The two factors that are identified by the law as being important in determining gravitational force, are the masses of the objects, and the distance between them. More specifically, the larger the masses and/or the closer the masses, then the larger the gravitational force.

Note that the law actually refers to particles, and therefore, whilst it is convenient to consider the mass of the object as a whole, and also to consider the distance between the centres of the two masses as representing the distance in the equation, this can lead to misinterpretations.

To all intents and purposes, the only object with a sufficiently large mass to produce observable changes in the motion of a sportsperson and/or piece of equipment, is the earth. The force which results from interactions with the earth is usually called **gravity**. Hence, if a ball is thrown into the air it is seen to be attracted back towards the planet's surface, and the same is true of a high jumper, pole vaulter, or gymnast, etc.

The gravitational force acting on a particular object is called its **weight** and this is clearly dependent on, but distinct from, the **mass** of an object. These terms are often used interchangeably but in fact have quite different meanings. Weight refers specifically to the gravitational force acting on the object, whilst mass refers to the amount of matter that actually makes up the object. If someone could do a vertical jump on the earth, and then on the moon, the mass of that person would be the same in both instances. However, the weight of the jumper would be considerably smaller on the moon because the jumper is interacting with a much smaller mass *(ie the moon)*, and therefore the gravitational force *(weight)* acting on the jumper would be smaller. It can be seen that for an athlete whose event involves a significant vertical motion *(eg high jump)* it is especially advantageous to reduce any excess body mass such as fat and to minimise the mass of kit such as clothes and shoes.

❖ *Sports Mechanics Application*

Normally, when considering sport situations on earth, the weight of an object or person is considered to be constant, and this assumption will be adopted in the rest of this text. However, it is of interest to note that because the earth is not a regular sphere, and that sports events take place at a variety of altitudes, there is some possibility of variation in the distance between particles as identified in Newton's law. Dyson (1986) suggests that if all other factors were equal, a 7.92 m long jump performed in Germany would be equivalent to a jump of 7.95 m in Kenya.

2.3 NEWTON'S FIRST LAW

Before proceeding to examine contact forces, it is necessary to introduce some additional concepts, and develop further some that have already been discussed. In the previous section, the concept of mass was introduced. This attribute of an object is the major determinant of how an object's motion will be affected by the presence or absence of a force. Newton developed three laws which identify the relationship between force and motion. The first of these is called the 'Law of Inertia' which may be stated as follows.

Every object will continue in a state of uniform motion in a straight line (or *remain at rest*) unless compelled to change its state of motion by a net external force acting on it.

This law indicates that an object has a natural reluctance to change its current state of motion. If it is moving in a straight line it will have a natural tendency to continue moving in a straight line at a constant speed. If it is stationary it will have a natural tendency to remain at rest. It is the reluctance to change its state of motion that is referred to as an object's **inertia**.

There are several points that need to be made.

a) As it is the **reluctance to change** attribute which describes inertia, an object does not lose, gain or overcome inertia. The only way that an object can change its inertia is if it loses or gains some mass. From this it can be seen that it is mass that determines the inertial characteristics of an object within the context of linear motion. If an object's mass remains the same then so does its inertia. One of the significant implications for sports performers is that any excess mass will give them a larger inertia and therefore inhibit rapid changes in speed and/or direction.

b) The law makes it clear that the natural behaviour of objects is to move in a straight line with constant speed. This implies that if an object is increasing its speed, decreasing its speed, and/or changing direction then there must be a net external force acting.

c) Before Newton it was thought that if motion was present then there must be a force acting. However, Newton's First Law indicates that this is not necessarily the case. If an object is moving in a straight line at a constant speed, then according to the first law, it is not experiencing a net force. Subjective experience in observing every day motion events may seem to contradict this. For example, if a ball is kicked it does not continue to roll for ever. However, the behaviour of the ball in coming to rest does not contradict Newton's Law, as it does in fact experience a net force *(friction)*. People not trained in mechanics may not always be aware of all the forces that are present.

When observing movement in the real world there are always a number of forces acting *(although in some cases they may be very small)*, and this can make it difficult to appreciate the principle of Newton's First Law.

The following examples illustrate how Newton's First Law may be applied within the context of sport. When reading the examples remember the Law of Inertia implies the following.

That if an object is speeding up, slowing down and/or changing direction,then it must be experiencing a net force.

Consider an example based on an ice hockey puck.

Phase 1 - Imagine an ice hockey puck at rest on the surface of the ice. Although it may not be possible to identify all the forces acting on the puck at this point, it should be clear that the net effect of any forces that are acting on it must be zero as the puck's motion is not changing.

Phase 2 - The puck now has a force applied to it when it is hit by an ice hockey stick. During the period of time that the stick is in contact with the puck, the puck changes its state of motion from one of being at rest to one of forward motion.

Phase 3 - As soon as contact between the stick and the puck is broken the force is no longer present, and the puck will then continue to travel in a straight line at a constant speed. *(There will inevitably be some small friction forces between the puck and the ice, and between the puck and the surrounding air, which will slow the puck down a little, but these effects will be ignored for the present).*

Phase 4 - The puck will continue to travel down the rink until another significant force is applied. This will occur when it hits the side of the ice rink. During the period of contact, the puck experiences a force which changes the puck's direction, and causes it to rebound with a new speed.

Phase 5 - Once the contact with the side wall has been broken the force ceases to be applied to the puck so it will once again continue to travel in a straight line with a constant speed.

Consider now the example of a sprinter who is in the set position on the blocks. The sprinter is stationary and must interact with the blocks in order to generate a force to change the stationary state of motion into forward motion.

The mechanism by which the sprinter achieves this may not be clear as yet, but there is no doubt that a force is applied to the sprinter. Anyone who has watched a sprint race observes the rapid change in the state of motion of the sprinter at the start of a race.

The changes in the sprinter's motion in the middle part of the race are not so significant, and require a detailed consideration of the forces that act on each footfall. *(This analysis will be conducted later in section 2.8.)*

At the end of the race when the runner stops, it is again apparent that the athlete's state of motion has changed and therefore a net external force must have been applied. Note that the inertia of the runner remains the same throughout the race.

2.4 NEWTON'S SECOND LAW

In continuing the investigation of force it is necessary to introduce the concept of **momentum**. If the question 'how much motion does an object have?' is asked, then the intuitive answer of the lay person often involves the concept of speed or velocity. However, this is an incomplete way of quantifying motion. Consider the following question. 'If a 110 kg prop forward and a 65 kg fly half are both running with a ball at a speed of 6 m·s^{-1}, which has the greater quantity of motion?' For a player who had to tackle the prop or fly half, the question itself reveals that a consideration of speed or velocity alone is not sufficient to describe the quantity of motion, but that the mass of the object must also be taken into account. The definition of momentum incorporates these two parameters in the following way:

Linear Momentum = Mass × Velocity

Consideration of the formula shows that an arrow shot from an archer's bow has a large momentum despite having a relatively small mass, and similarly a set of eight rugby forwards pushing a scrummaging machine, even slowly, have a large momentum.

Newton's Second Law uses this concept and may be stated as follows.

The rate of change of momentum of an object (*or acceleration of an object of fixed mass*) **is directly proportional to the force causing the change, and the resulting change in momentum takes place in the direction in which the force was applied.** ie:

$$\overline{F} = \frac{(m_f \times v_f) - (m_i \times v_i)}{t}$$

where:

$\overline{F}$ = average force;
m_f = mass at end of time interval;
m_i = mass at start of time interval;
v_f = velocity at end of time interval;
v_i = velocity at start of time interval;
t = time interval.

This is a fairly complicated definition and formula and needs to be considered carefully. Taking the previous discussion of the Newton's First Law together with the definition above, it is now possible to state the following.

A force is required to change the momentum of an object.

In fact, Newton's Second Law indicates, that the rate at which an object loses or gains momentum, is directly related to the applied force.

A stationary golf ball on a tee experiences a large force over a short period of time when struck by a golf club, and therefore the rate at which the momentum of the golf ball is changed is very high. However, this example tells only half the story, because the second law indicates that the change in momentum will take place in the direction of the applied force. In the case of the stationary golf ball this may be clear, but the situation where an object is already moving (*ie. already has some momentum*) before the force is applied, also needs to be considered.

Momentum has the properties of a vector, namely, magnitude and direction. Therefore in exploring the problem of what happens to an object which already has some momentum when a force is applied, it is best to use vector arrow representation.

Figure 2.1 shows three soccer players A, B and C. Training has been set up so that player A is to pass the ball to player B who must pass the ball with only one touch to player C. The path of the ball would therefore be as shown in **Figure 2.1**.

Figure 2.1: *Required path of the ball between three soccer players as seen from above.*

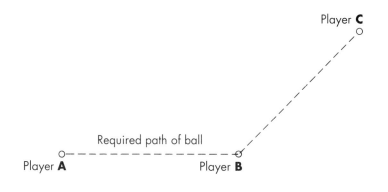

When the ball arrives at player B it already has some momentum, and this will be in the direction determined by the force applied by player A *(assuming there are no external forces between player A and B)*. If player B now applies a force to the ball, according to Newton's Second Law the ball will gain momentum in the direction of the applied force. If the force is directed towards player C then the new momentum will be gained in this direction, **Figure 2.2**.

Figure 2.2: *Original and new linear momentum vectors of the ball.*

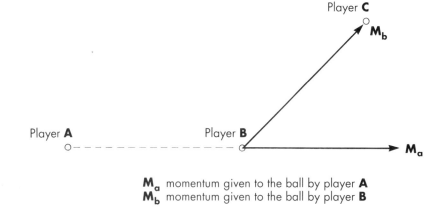

M_a momentum given to the ball by player **A**
M_b momentum given to the ball by player **B**

The resultant momentum of the ball may be obtained by constructing a parallelogram, and it is the direction of the resultant that will indicate the direction of travel of the ball. For the situation described above the resultant would be as shown in **Figure 2.3**. In this situation the ball would fail to arrive at player C.

Figure 2.3: *Resultant momentum vector indicating the direction of travel of the ball. Note that the direction of the resultant momentum vector indicates the direction the ball will actually travel. The desired direction is that indicated by mb.*

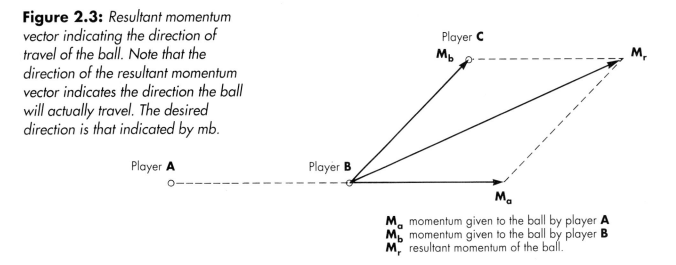

M_a momentum given to the ball by player **A**
M_b momentum given to the ball by player **B**
M_r resultant momentum of the ball.

Note that for a successful pass, the force applied by player B should not be directed towards player C but as shown in **Figure 2.4**.

Figure 2.4: *Required momentum components to give a resultant momentum in the desired direction.*

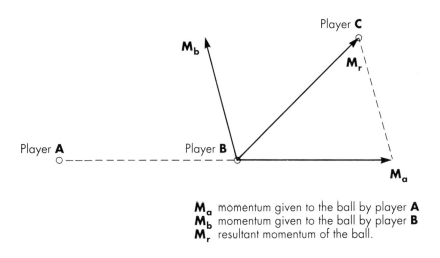

M_a momentum given to the ball by player **A**
M_b momentum given to the ball by player **B**
M_r resultant momentum of the ball.

The interpretation of Newton's Second Law can be considered from a different point of view if the mass of the object being investigated is assumed to be constant. In most sports situations this is a reasonable assumption, and therefore the second law may be summarised by the formula:

$$\overline{F} = m \times \left(\frac{v_f - v_i}{t}\right)$$

The element of this equation inside the square brackets is in fact the formula for acceleration and therefore the equation may further be simplified to:

$$\overline{F} = m \times \overline{a}$$

where:

$\overline{F}$ = average force;

m = mass;

$\overline{a}$ = average acceleration.

This equation simply states that the acceleration an object experiences will be directly proportional to the force applied. When the force may be considered to act at an instant, then the equation simply becomes:

$$F = m \times a$$

It is this form of the equation which is often used to define the unit of measurement for force – a newton *(N)*. This is defined as:

the force required to give a mass of one kilogram an acceleration of one metre per second per second.

It is worth emphasising the direct relationship between force and acceleration, and it is also appropriate to briefly return to consider the effects of gravitational force.

It was noted earlier *(section 2.2)* that for objects of fixed mass the gravitational force *(weight)* remains constant. According then to Newton's Second Law, the acceleration of an object when it is only under the influence of gravity will also be constant, and this indeed is the case. In fact, because the gravitational force that an object experiences is directly proportional to its mass, all objects accelerate at approximately $9.8 \ m \cdot s^{-2}$ when gravity is the only influencing force. This can be observed more clearly if the basic formula is rearranged in the following way.

$$\frac{F}{m} = a$$

In this case 'F' represents gravitational force, 'm' the mass of the object, and 'a' the acceleration due to gravity. The formula shows that if 'F' and 'm' are proportionally related, as is the case when considering gravity, then 'a' will be a constant. This relationship therefore implies that if two divers with different masses were to jump from a high diving position at the same time, they would both hit the water at the same instant *(assuming the influence of air resistance is ignored)*.

Consider the acceleration that a ball experiences when it is thrown up into the air. If it is assumed that air resistance is negligible, then the only force that the ball experiences once it has left the thrower's hand is gravity.

Table **2.1** shows how the velocity of the ball changes from the moment it leaves the thrower's hand to the moment it is caught. The data assume that the ball is thrown vertically and is caught at the same height at which it was released.

Table **2.1** also shows that during the period of flight, the ball experiences a constant acceleration, which is exactly what Newton's Second Law would predict. It is important to reflect on, and note that, the ball's speed and direction change during the flight, but the acceleration remains constant.

Table 2.1: *Change in velocity of a ball thrown up into the air.*

Time from release (s)	Velocity $(m \cdot s^{-1})$	Accel. $(m \cdot s^{-2})$
0.0	14.7	
		–9.8
1.0	4.9	
		–9.8
1.5	0.0	
		–9.8
2.0	–4.9	
		–9.8
3.0	–14.7	

Figure 2.5: *Graph showing the relationship between force and acceleration for an object with a fixed mass.*

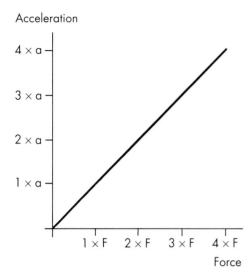

Note that the upwards direction is taken to be positive, and the fact that the acceleration is shown to be negative throughout the flight indicates that the force was acting in a downwards direction, which of course gravity does.

The key factor to note in the above example is that the observed acceleration of an object will be proportional to the net force acting on the object at any particular time. This is not just true for situations where the force is constant but applies to all force situations.

Consider **Figure 2.5** which shows the relationship between force and acceleration when a force is applied to a fixed mass at a series of increasing values.

Figure 2.5 shows that if you double the magnitude of the force, then you double the magnitude of the acceleration that the object will experience. If you triple the magnitude of the force, then you triple the acceleration that the object will experience, and so on.

2.5 NEWTON'S THIRD LAW

Newton's Third Law may formally be stated as follows.

'When one object exerts a force on a second object there is a force equal in magnitude but opposite in direction exerted by the second object on the first.'

This is frequently is called the action/reaction law, which is an easy to remember catch phrase, but for the purpose of analysing sports movements, reference needs to be made to the full definition outlined above.

There are a number of important points which need to be considered when making interpretations using this law.

The law refers to **two** objects, and therefore it is important when making interpretations to identify the two objects that are involved in the interaction. The action/reaction forces may be considered as a pair, but they never act as a pair on the same object. *(Note that 'object' here refers to the system which defines forces to be external or internal.)* Consider the following example.

The sprinter on the blocks referred to earlier was shown to experience a force driving him/her forwards. From Newton's Third Law it can now be seen that the force driving the sprinter forwards must be matched by an equal but opposite force acting on the blocks. The two objects in this example are the sprinter and the blocks, but as the blocks are attached to the surface of the planet, the second object is effectively the planet.

One of the reasons why it is important to identify the two objects can be made clear if reference is made to Newton's Second Law. The sprinter experiences a force which causes him/her to

COLEG MENAI

ANGOR, GWYNEDD LL57 2

accelerate. The blocks experience exactly the same force in terms of magnitude but opposite in direction, and because the effective mass of the blocks is that of the planet, any acceleration would be insignificant *(also the planet is experiencing millions of other interactions)*.

The 'action/reaction' phrase can seem to imply that the action is followed by the reaction. This is **not** an appropriate interpretation as the action/reaction forces should be considered as acting at the same time.

One further example may help when interpreting situations where several forces are acting.

Earlier *(section 2.3)* an example was cited where an ice puck was resting on the surface of an ice rink. The force of gravity is clearly one force that must have been acting on the puck. According to Newton's Third Law, the rink *(planet)* as the other object in the interaction must have been experiencing an equal but opposite force.

However, this only identifies one force acting on the puck. As the puck is not accelerating when it is at rest on the ice surface, there must be at least one other force acting to neutralise the identified gravitational force.

Whenever two objects are in contact with one another then there is force present as a result of this interaction. In this case the puck exerts a force on the surface of the ice, and in accordance with Newton's Third Law, the puck experiences an equal but opposite force. Therefore the puck when at rest is experiencing two forces, the gravitational force *(which is acting independently of any contact)* and the contact reaction force.

Although **Figure 2.6** shows that the puck experiences two equal and opposite forces, it should be noted that this is not an action/reaction pair as defined by Newton's Third Law, as both forces are acting on the **same** object.

Figure 2.6: *Forces acting on an ice hockey puck at rest.*

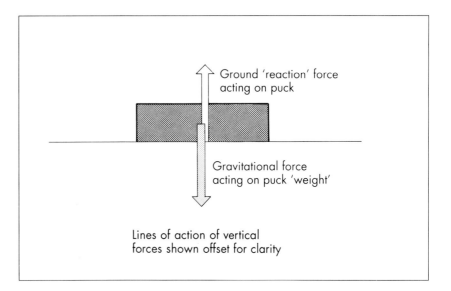

Ground 'reaction' force
acting on puck

Gravitational force
acting on puck 'weight'

Lines of action of vertical
forces shown offset for clarity

2.6 NET FORCE

One important factor to stress in the last example, is that when considering a motion situation all the forces acting must be taken into account, because the observed state of motion at any particular instant will reflect the net force acting at that moment.

In the case of the ice puck resting on the surface of the ice, the net force was zero, because the vertical forces acting on the puck cancelled each other out, and no horizontal forces were present. However, when the ice hockey stick strikes the puck, an additional force is introduced, causing the puck to accelerate during the period of time the stick and puck are in contact: **Figure 2.7.**

Figure 2.7: *Forces acting on an ice hockey puck whilst being struck by an ice hockey stick.*

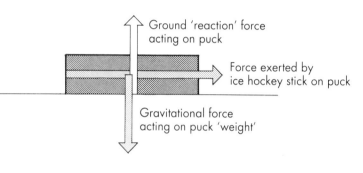

Ground 'reaction' force acting on puck

Force exerted by ice hockey stick on puck

Gravitational force acting on puck 'weight'

Lines of action of vertical forces shown offset for clarity

It is important to note that once contact between the stick and the puck is broken, there is a zero net force situation again, and therefore according to Newton's First Law, the puck will continue to travel at a constant velocity. *(Note that this example assumes that there is no friction between the puck and the ice)*. In considering this example it should be noted that the zero net force situation may exist both when the puck is stationary **and** when it is moving. In circumstances where an object is stationary and experiencing a net zero force situation it is said to be in a state of **static equilibrium.** Where an object is moving but experiencing a net zero force situation it is said to be in a state of **dynamic equilibrium.**

It is appropriate at this point in the text to remind the reader that in order to simplify the examples, the effects of fluid forces have not been taken into account in the preceding analysis of net forces.

Fluid forces are those that arise as a result of the interaction of a sportsperson or implement with fluids such as air and water. In some cases, for example javelin and swimming, their effects are particularly important, whilst in other events such as shot put the effects are small. In a full analysis of the net force acting in a sport situation these fluid forces would need to be taken into account. A simple account of fluid forces appears in Chapter 6.

Examples used so far have focussed largely on sports implements of one kind or another. The next section, which continues the investigation of force, will draw its examples from basic sports movements such as running and jumping.

When considering activities which involve a human performer, it is important to appreciate that the system being considered is very complex, and therefore it is often necessary to make some simplifying assumptions. In some events it might be reasonable to assume that the human body is a single rigid object, for example in a high board dive during the 'toppling' phase of the take off. However, the number of events that can be satisfactorily modelled in this way is very limited. In the following examples a different approach is used, where it is assumed that it is reasonable to model the human body as a series of inter-connected rigid links, with each link having a fixed mass, and with the associated joints modelled as pin joints. An artists 'lay figure' gives a good impression of the human body modelled in this way as shown in **Figure 2.8**.

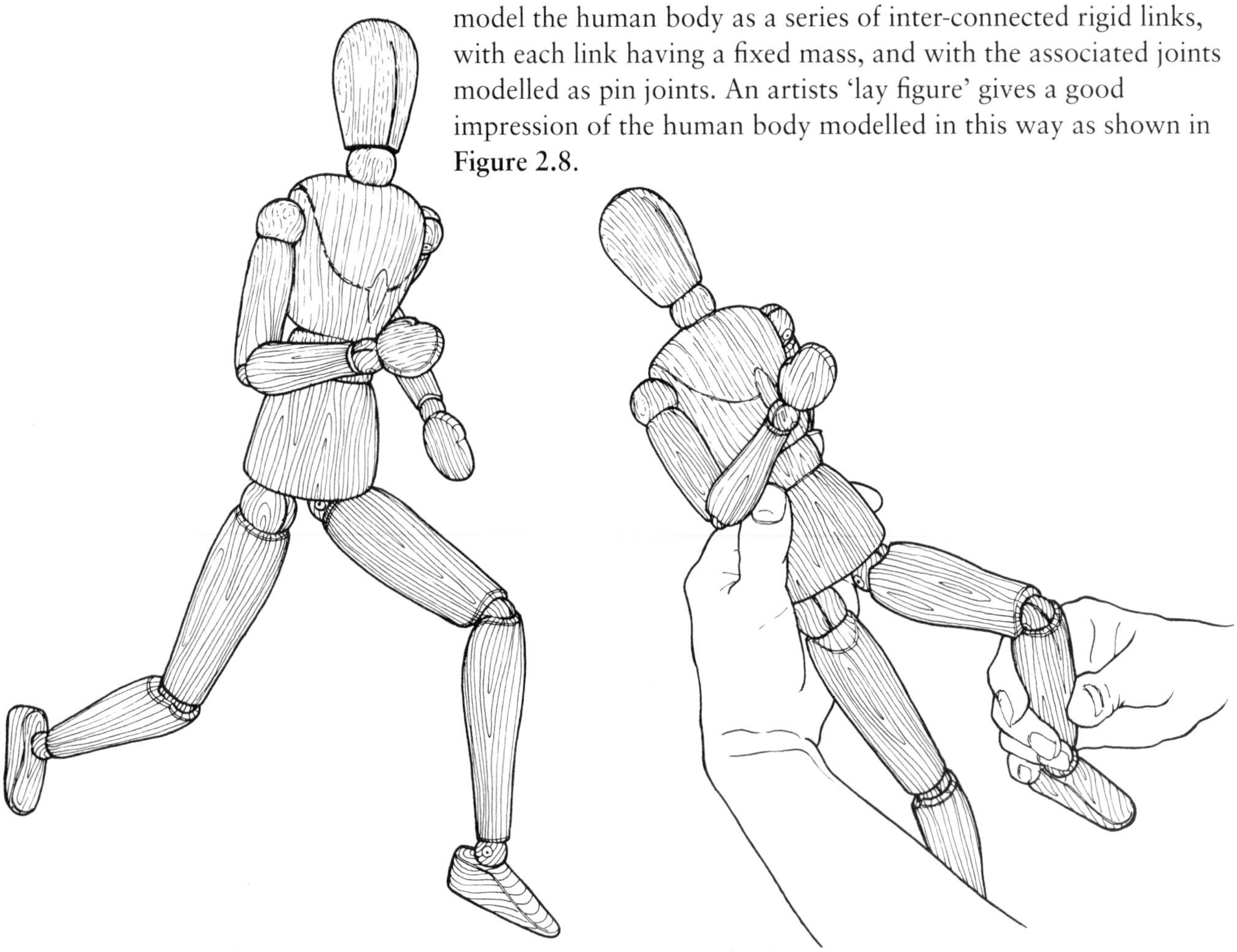

Figure 2.8: *An artists 'lay figure'.*

With the body modelled in this way it is possible to investigate how changes in the motion of body segments are related to ground reaction forces. This is especially important in many sports where special techniques are required to move the performer's body in the most effective way in order to achieve the objective of the sport. Good examples are athletics jumping and running events, but large numbers of other sports also have the same basic requirements. It is important to note that the link model is not the only one which is helpful in explaining human movement. In later sections it will be appropriate to model the body as a single particle.

Earlier in this Chapter *(section 2.1)* it was noted that, in order to explain observed changes in the motion of a 'system of interest', the external forces acting on that system need to be identified. In cases where the sports performer is the 'system of interest' and is in contact with the ground or another fixed object, the external forces that need to be considered are gravity and 'ground' reaction forces. Note that other fixed surfaces such as vaulting boxes can equally be considered to transmit 'ground' reaction forces; and that fluid forces, such as air resistance, are for the moment ignored.

A performer, when in contact with a supporting surface, is acted upon by two external forces which can account for changes in his/her total body motion. The direction and magnitude of one of these forces, gravity, remains the same throughout any performance. It may be recalled that this is the case because the gravitational force acting on the performer, which is termed his/her weight, is dependent on the mass of the performer, the mass of the planet, and the distance between the performer and planet. Therefore, unless any of these factors changes during the performance, *(which is normally assumed **not** to be the case)*, the weight of the performer *(gravitational force)* will remain constant.

The ground reaction force, unlike weight, will change in association with changes in motion of the body segments. An easy way to observe that this is the case, is to stand on a set of bathroom scales with your arms placed behind your back. Remain still for a moment and then vigorously swing your arms forward. You will notice that the value recorded on the scales varies considerably. You may also be able to notice that, at some points in the swing the value was greater than it was at the start when you were still, and at other points it was smaller. The important point to note is that the arm swing was associated with the scales experiencing a varying magnitude of force. In accordance with Newton's Third Law there must be an equal and opposite force acting on you: the ground reaction force *(scales reaction force!)*.

It may now be noted that the force transmitted to the ground *(and the corresponding ground reaction force)* is dependent on the masses and accelerations of the segments of the body. The accelerations of the segments are directly caused by the combined effects of gravity and muscle force, and the resultant of all segmental accelerations is associated with the performer pushing with greater or lesser force against the supporting surface.

This last point indicates that different segments of the body can have different accelerations at a particular moment in time, but it is the combined effect of these segmental accelerations that determines the precise nature of the interaction between the supporting surface and the performer. In the case of the arm swing on the scales, only the arms were involved, but in a sports event *(or indeed in most human body movement)*, many more segments are involved. A sports performer can adjust the timing and sequencing of segmental accelerations *(which can be thought of as his/her technique)* and this will vary the magnitude and direction of the ground reaction force that s/he experiences. One of the key features of highly skilled performers in many sports events is their ability to develop techniques which enable them to generate optimal ground reaction forces.

It may now be noted that the net external force acting on a performer, which is the resultant of the gravitational force and the ground reaction force, will cause an acceleration of the performer. In order to describe the acceleration of a complex system such as the human body it is necessary to use the concept of an imaginary point called the centre of gravity *(or centre of mass)*. This concept is covered in more detail later in this Chapter *(section 3.4)*, but at this stage it may be considered to be a point where the entire mass of the performer is concentrated. Changes in the motion of this imaginary point directly reflect the external forces acting on the defined system.

Before moving on to consider some specific examples in sport, it is worth reflecting on the significance of muscle force in the above explanation.

In undertaking a sport technique the performer uses some psychological representation *(e.g. a motor program)* to start and control the sequence and timing of the muscle actions. The muscle actions cause the body's segments to move according to the pattern prescribed by the psychological representation. However, in mechanical terms, as was highlighted earlier, the muscle forces on their own cannot be used to account for changes in the body's motion when the whole body is the system of interest. If this remains a difficult idea, it might be helpful to imagine an athlete who is placed in deep space away from the influence of gravity and any contact with a supporting surface. In such circumstances the athlete would not experience any external forces. The muscle forces could cause his/her segments to move in a pattern which exactly replicated the action of a skill like running, but the athlete would not experience any change in his/her linear velocity.

(The reader may choose to read section 3.4 on the centre of gravity/centre of mass before considering the examples that follow.)

2.6.1 FORCES ACTING IN THE TAKE OFF PHASE OF A VERTICAL JUMP

The following example considers a simple vertical jump movement and illustrates the relationship between the external forces at a number of discrete points in the jump. It should be noted that references to the acceleration of the jumper are in fact referring to the acceleration of the centre of gravity/centre of mass of the jumper. A vertical jump consists of a downward squat phase, followed by an extension of the knees and hips until the jumper leaves the ground in an extended position. Some form of arm swing is usually employed during the jump. The jumper spends a short time in the air, usually trying to reach for maximum height, before landing on the ground and returning to a stationary position. **Figure 2.9** shows a series of positions during the take off phase.

Figure 2.9: *Series of positions during the take off phase of a vertical jump.*

The analysis which follows considers the first part of the jump, up to the jumper leaving the floor. The analysis ignores any influences of air resistance, and assumes that the jump takes place in a completely vertical direction.

At the start of the jump when in a stationary position the forces acting on the jumper will be as shown in **Figure 2.10**.

Notice that the pair of forces are exactly the same as for the example of the ice hockey puck resting on the ice. That is the forces are of equal magnitude and opposite in direction, and therefore the jumper is experiencing a net zero force. As s/he is stationary and is not experiencing a net force, his/her velocity remains unchanged at this instant. *(Note that although the two forces are equal and opposite, because they are acting on the same object they are not an example of Newton's Third Law.)*

The jumper initially starts to move down at the start of the squat phase when some of his/her postural muscles are relaxed. As the jumper has started to move down, having originally been in a stationary position, there has been a change in his/her velocity, and therefore a net external force must be acting. In effect, body segments *(that is part of the body's mass)* are being allowed to fall towards the ground under the effects of gravity. This action is

Figure 2.10: *Forces acting on the jumper at the start of the jump.*

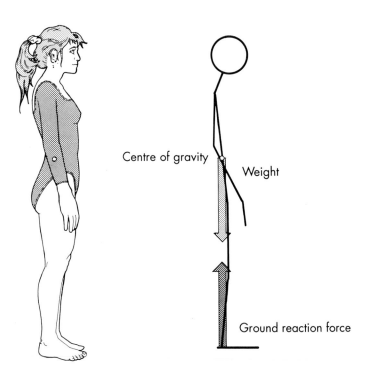

associated with a reduction in the ground reaction force. By standing on a set of bathroom scales and allowing your body to enter the squat phase you can observe the reduction in ground reaction. *(Note that it is the first significant movement of the scales that you are looking for.)*

The net external force at this point in the jump is therefore acting in a downwards direction. **Figure 2.11** shows the relationship between the gravitational force *(weight)* and ground reaction force at this point.

It should also be noted, that as the net force at this stage is acting downwards, the acceleration of the jumper will be negative at this point. This period of the jump is a very short one, because if the jumper allowed the situation to continue then s/he would end up as a pile on the floor!

Having acquired some downward momentum, the jumper tenses

Figure 2.11: *Relationship between the gravitational force (weight) and ground reaction force at the start of the squat phase of a simple vertical jump.*

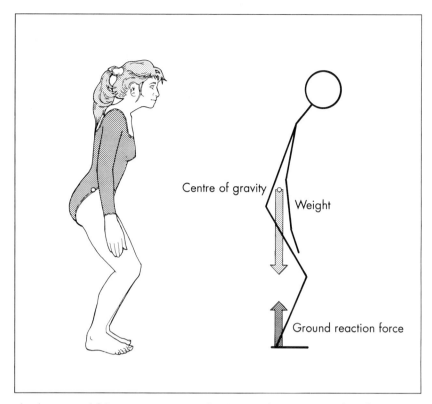

the knee and hip extensor muscles in combination with other muscle groups in the body. This action results in a large increase in the force being applied to the surface and an equal increase in ground reaction. The net force acting on the jumper is now in an upward direction. The relationship between the gravitational force *(weight)* and the ground reaction force for this point in the jump is shown in **Figure 2.12**.

The jumper, as shown in **Figure 2.12**, is experiencing a positive acceleration, but it should be noted that early on in this phase of the jump, the jumper will still be moving in a downward direction

Figure 2.12: *Relationship between the gravitational force (weight) and the ground reaction force.*

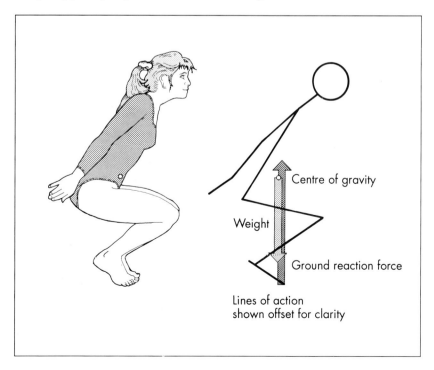

because the jumper had acquired some downward momentum prior to the large muscle groups being tensed, this downward momentum must be cancelled out prior to the jumper obtaining upward momentum.

The point of zero momentum *(and zero velocity)* occurs at the bottom of the squat phase, and from this point onwards the jumper will gain upward momentum, up to a point just prior to take off. The large muscle groups will continue to be highly active during this phase, and the net force during the major part of the upward motion of the jump will act in an upward direction Throughout the main part of this driving up phase, the relationship between the ground reaction force and gravity will be as shown in **Figure 2.13**.

Figure 2.13: *Relationship between the ground reaction force and gravity throughout the main part of the driving up phase of a vertical jump. Note that the relationship is unchanged from that shown in Figure 2.12. As the diagrams only show the forces acting at an instant, it is the fact that the ground reaction force is larger than weight at these points of the jump that is significant, rather than precise comparisons of force magnitudes.*

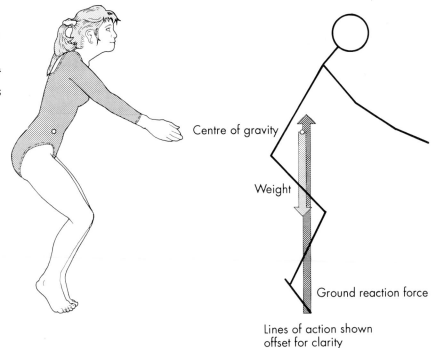

Centre of gravity

Weight

Ground reaction force

Lines of action shown offset for clarity

In the last few moments of the take off, the jumper will be close to a fully extended position, and will have upward momentum taking him/her away from surface. The jumper will be unable to push against the surface and therefore only a small ground reaction force is generated whilst contact remains. As the net force during this stage is downwards the jumper experiences a negative acceleration and will in fact be losing vertical velocity. The relationship between gravitational force *(weight)* and ground reaction force for this end phase of the jump is shown in **Figure 2.14**.

Once the jumper leaves the ground s/he will only experience the downward force of gravity, and therefore will continue to experience a negative acceleration, until contact with the ground is made once again .

Figure 2.14: *Relationship between gravitational force (weight) and ground reaction force at the end of the take off phase of a vertical jump.*

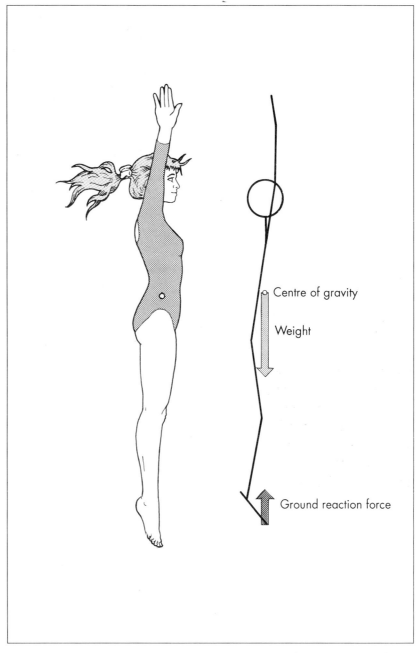

This example shows how the ground reaction force *(contact force)* may vary in human movement situations. However, the diagrams only indicate the forces acting at particular instants, and in situations where ground reaction contact forces are variable, it is often more useful to consider how the forces change with respect to a period of time rather than at particular moments in time. If you have experimented with the bathroom scales you will have noticed that the ground reaction force changes as actions occur over a period of time. The next section considers force changes with respect to time, and introduces some new concepts which will help to explain the changes in movement that are observed in sport situations.

Figure 2.15 shows the pattern of the vertical ground reaction force as it varies with time for a vertical jump. Consider the phases of the graph as follows.

Figure 2.15: *Graph showing the vertical ground reaction force during the take off phase of a vertical jump.*

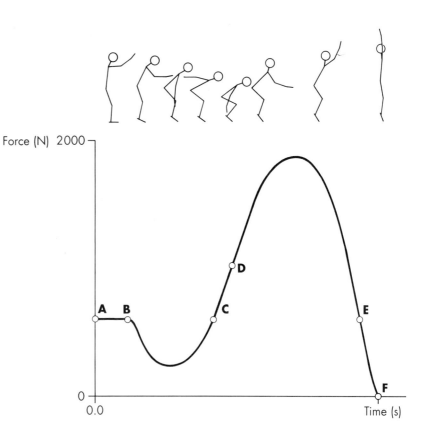

A–B. The ground reaction force during this phase remains constant at a value equal to the jumper's body weight and represents the point where the jumper is standing still, before the jump.

B–C. The ground reaction force is smaller than the athlete's weight and so the jumper experiences a net downwards force.

C–D. At C the jumper will have acquired the maximum downward velocity, and for an instant experiences a net zero force. After point C the ground reaction force continues to rise. Initially the jumper will still be travelling downwards *(see previous discussion)*, but at point D will have reached the bottom of the squat phase. It should be noted that there is no significant characteristic of the ground reaction force trace itself which identifies this point of the jump.

D–E. During this phase the jumper will be driving upwards and experiences a net upwards force. Ground reaction force will be larger than gravitational force.

E–F. At point E the jumper experiences a net zero force for an instant, and the jumper will reach maximum vertical velocity at this point. The trace continues the trend of the previous phase, and reduces to zero at the point of take off. During this phase the net force acting on the jumper is in a downward direction.

Before continuing the analysis of the jump it will be helpful to introduce the concept of impulse.

2.7 IMPULSE

Earlier *(section 2.4)* it was seen that for an object of constant mass Newton's Second Law could be written as:

$$\overline{F} = m \times \frac{(v_f - v_i)}{t}$$

where:

$\overline{F}$ = average force;
t = time interval;
m = mass (constant);
v_f = velocity at end of time interval;
v_i = velocity at start of time interval.

This formula can be re-written to give:

$$\overline{F} \times t = (m \times v_f) - (m \times v_i)$$

This is sometimes known as the Impulse-Momentum equation. The term on the left *(Ft)* being defined as the **impulse** of the force, and the term on the right as the change in momentum experienced by the object as a result of the impulse. A further rearrangement of the formula *(again assuming the mass to be constant)* gives:

$$\frac{\overline{F} \times t}{m} = v_f - v_i$$

This formula now indicates that the impulse divided by the mass is equal to the **change** in velocity experienced by the object. Note that as time approaches a very small value, force may be considered to be an instantaneous value.

❖ *Sports Mechanics Application*

High jumpers need to generate a large vertical velocity in order to project themselves over the bar. To do this they need to generate a large impulse during take off. To assist in this they try to take a long and low last stride into the take off phase of the jump. Because the body is in a relatively low position, the ground reaction force has the potential to act over a longer period of time before the jumper breaks contact with the ground. This increases the potential of the jumper to generate a large impulse. In addition, if the last stride is long and low, the vertical velocity of the jumper at the point when the take off foot touches the ground can be kept small (although it normally remains negative around -0.4 m·s^{-1} for elite jumpers). Ideally this vertical velocity would be zero or even positive but this is very difficult to achieve. With only a small negative vertical velocity, the change in velocity which results from the impulse will be effective in giving the jumper a high positive vertical velocity at take off, which is what the jumper requires.

(Dapena 1987)

If the graph of the vertical ground reaction force for a vertical jump, **Figure 2.15,** is now reconsidered, it may be noted that the vertical axis represents force and the horizontal axis time. Therefore, on the graph, force × time is represented by the area under the curve. This is shown in **Figure 2.16.**

Figure 2.16: *Graph showing the vertical ground reaction force during the take off phase of a vertical jump.*

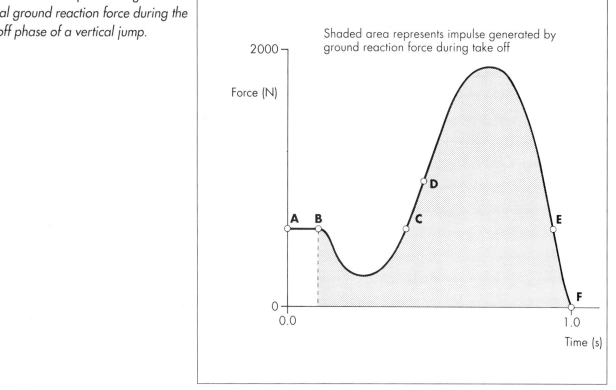

Figure 2.16: *Graph showing the vertical ground reaction force during the take off phase of a vertical jump.*

It must be noted that the jumper will also be experiencing the force of gravity, and this will also be acting as an impulse but in a downward direction. Therefore, to explain the jump in terms of the Impulse-Momentum relationship, an appreciation of the net force acting on the jumper is needed: **Figures 2.17** to **2.19** illustrate this.

Figure 2.17: *Graph showing impulses generated by the vertical ground reaction force and gravitational force during the take off phase of a vertical jump.*

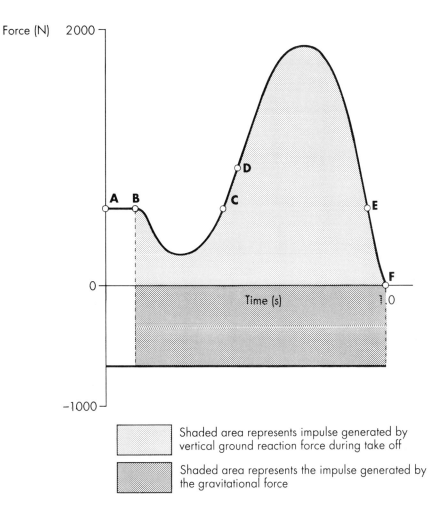

Shaded area represents impulse generated by vertical ground reaction force during take off

Shaded area represents the impulse generated by the gravitational force

It is the combined effect of the gravitational force, and the vertical ground reaction, that causes the net change in the jumper's momentum. To represent this on the graph, the gravitational impulse can be overlayed on to the ground reaction force impulse. Remembering that the gravitational impulse is effectively negative, the net impulse is represented by the areas of the graph shown in **Figure 2.18** which show single shading, as the crossed areas represent impulse values that have effectively cancelled each other out.

Figure 2.18: *Graph showing superimposed ground reaction and gravitational impulse representations.*

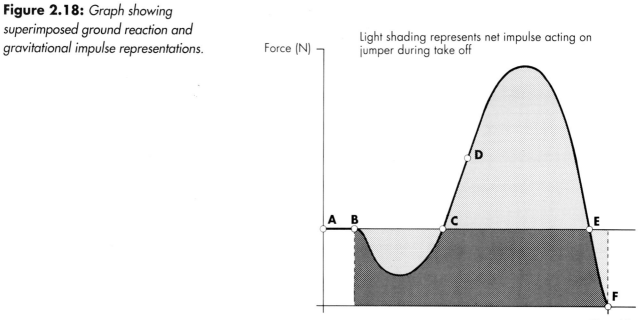

Force (N)

Light shading represents net impulse acting on jumper during take off

A B   C   E

F

Time (s)

Figure 2.19: *Graph showing a representation of the net impulse acting during the take off phase of a vertical jump.*

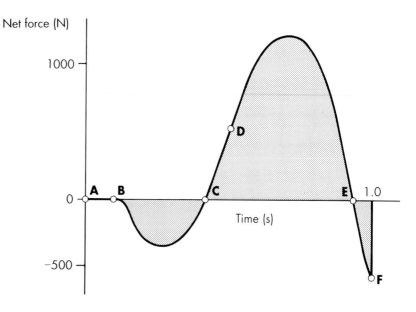

Net force (N)

1000 –

D

0 – A B   C   E 1.0

Time (s)

–500 –

F

The sum of the positive and negative areas in this diagram gives the net impulse in units of newton seconds *(N·s)*.

The formula identified earlier, and shown below, can now be used to examine the jumper's velocity:

$$\frac{\overline{F} \times t}{m} = v_f - v_i$$

If the net impulse value is divided by the jumper's mass, the change in vertical velocity of the jumper is obtained.

Because the jumper started with zero velocity then the change in this case gives the actual take off velocity of the jumper.

If the above process was applied at a series of small time intervals from the start of the jump, then instead of only having the change in velocity at the take off point, a picture of the changes in velocity could be built up over the whole period of time during the take off. A vertical velocity versus time graph could be then be plotted and would look like that shown in **Figure 2.20**.

Figure 2.20: *Graph showing the vertical velocity of a jumper during the take off phase of a vertical jump.*

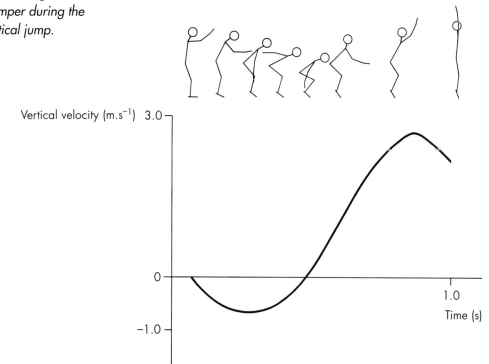

❖ *Sports Mechanics Application*

Several sports involve a vertical jump technique, e.g. rugby line out jumping, a basketball tip off, basketball rebounding, heading a soccer ball, volleyball blocking, etc. Sport scientists have used vertical force traces to calculate the take off vertical velocities obtained using these techniques. Two different techniques that can be used, are the counter movement technique where the jumper moves down immediately before extension of the knee joint, and a non counter movement technique where the jumper starts with legs already bent. Results from investigations have varied (Lees and Fahmi 1983), but normally the counter movement technique is considered to produce the highest vertical velocity and thus would appear to have the greatest potential to help a performer gain height. However it is important to note that if the skill also involves a reaching technique (e.g. basketball tip off) whilst in the air, any benefit from the take off technique could be lost by poor timing. The performer may also have tactical decisions to make which prevent him/her from using a particular technique, or they may simply have a psychological preference for using a particular technique.

2.8 FORCES AND RUNNING

In order to revise and develop the ideas on force that have been introduced so far it will be useful to consider the external forces responsible for the changes in motion observed to occur in running.

In running, the forces that are important are ground reaction force, weight, and air resistance. Although air resistance is sometimes important in competitive running, particularly in sprinting where restrictions exist on following wind speeds for world record ratification, in the analysis that follows its influence will not be considered.

One of the major differences between the analysis of running compared to that of the vertical jump, is that there is a horizontal component to the ground reaction force. In most situations in sport, when the performer interacts with the ground they will evoke a ground reaction which contains such a horizontal component. Indeed, the ground reaction may be considered in three dimensions, with two horizontal components and a vertical component as shown in **Figure 2.21**.

The discussion so far in this section has firmly established that a force is necessary to change an object's motion. The major changes that occur in running are in a horizontal direction, and therefore an understanding of horizontal ground reaction force is vital.

The forces applied by the runner in a forward and backward *(anterior-posterior)* direction *(Fy)*, are the most important in propelling and stopping the runner, but before examining these

Figure 2.21: *Graph showing the three orthogonal components of a ground reaction force.*

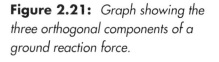

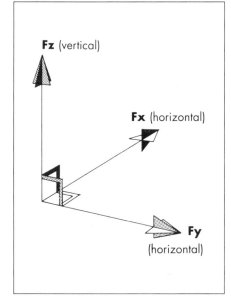

forces in detail consideration will be given to the side to side *(medio-lateral)* direction *(Fx)* horizontal forces.

If the runner pushes against the ground s/he will experience an equal but opposite reaction *(Newton's Third Law)*. Even when running with a normal style in a straight line, the runner will generate side to side forces, although they tend to be very small and individual in their pattern. However, it is important to remember that a change in motion, not only relates to the increase or decrease in forward speed of the runner, but also to the change in direction of the runner. It is in this latter situation that the side to side forces are particularly important.

An athlete running around a bend, must push on the ground towards the outside of the bend in order that s/he experiences a reaction force directed towards the centre of the bend. It is this force, directed towards the centre of the bend, that causes the runner's change of direction around the bend.

It should be noted, that as the runner is experiencing a net force *(which is causing the change of direction)* s/he is also experiencing the corresponding acceleration. This is the case even if the runner is not increasing his/her forward speed.

Any changes in the runner's forward speed when travelling in a straight path are caused by the forward-backward component of the ground reaction force. This force will be considered within the context of a 100 m sprint race, which starts from a set of blocks and finishes at the end of a 100 m straight. In the force diagrams and descriptions that follow, positive forces are those considered to act on the runner in the direction of the run, and negative forces are those considered to act on the runner in the opposite direction to that of the run.

As the gun is fired at the start of the race, the runner pushes back hard against the ground *(or blocks)* in order to generate a large reaction force. This generates a large forward impulse as illustrated in **Figure 2.22**.

Figure 2.22: *Graph showing horizontal ground reaction force trace acting on a sprinter whilst pushing against the starting blocks. The shaded area represents the horizontal impulse acting on the runner whilst in contact with the starting blocks.*

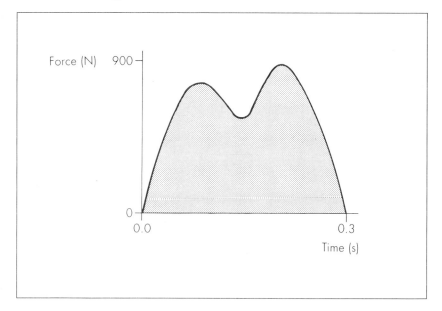

The force curve shown in **Figure 2.22** is typical for the start of a sprint race, and shows the influence of the rear foot in the first part of the trace, followed by the front foot drive .

As the component of force is a horizontal one, there is no gravitational component to consider, and therefore the impulse as represented by the area under the curve will generate a change in the runner's velocity, from zero to some positive value *(see vertical jump impulse analysis)*.

On leaving the blocks, the runner generates ground reaction forces with each succeeding footfall. In the early part of the race a typical force trace from one footfall would look like that shown in **Figure 2.23**.

Figure 2.23: *Graph showing the horizontal ground reaction force acting on a sprinter for one footfall early in a 100 m race. The shaded area represents impulse acting on runner during foot contact.*

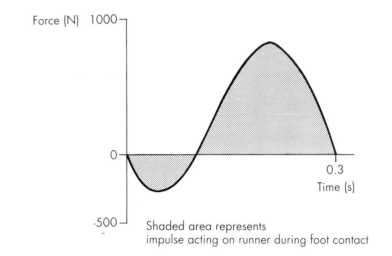

It is important to note that as the foot makes contact with the ground, the reaction force is actually acting against the direction of the run *(as indicated by the negative value)*, but as the body moves over the supporting foot then the force acting on the runner is directed forwards.

The significance of the trace can best be appreciated by considering the impulse generated during the contact. In the first part of the contact the impulse is negative, and therefore the runner loses forward momentum, (and as the runner's mass does not change this may be expressed as a loss in forward velocity).

The second half of the trace shows a positive impulse indicating an increase in forward velocity. It can also be seen from the trace that the positive change in velocity is larger than the negative change, and therefore the runner experiences a net increase in forward velocity during this footfall. This is exactly what would be expected during the early part of the race.

During the middle of the race a typical trace would be like that shown in **Figure 2.24**.

Figure 2.24: *Graph showing the horizontal ground reaction force acting on a sprinter for one footfall in the middle stages of a 100 m race. The shaded area represents the impulse acting on the runner during foot contact with the ground.*

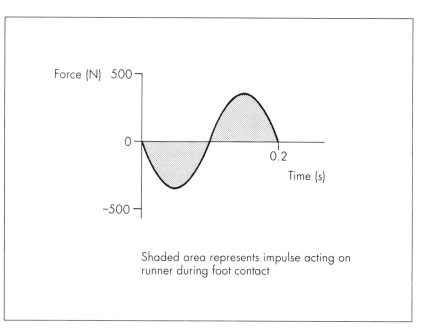

Shaded area represents impulse acting on runner during foot contact

It should be noticed, once again, that the runner experiences a force acting backwards on him/her during the first part of the contact, but that this changes to a forward acting force during the second half of the contact. Examination of the impulse shows that the negative area matches the positive area, and therefore the runner is experiencing a net zero change in velocity. This would suggest, that in terms of the race, the runner has reached a maximum velocity, and is neither losing or gaining velocity over the complete footfall.

At the end of the race the runner may well be beginning to tire slightly, in which case the force trace may well look like the one shown in **Figure 2.25**.

An examination of the trace in **Figure 2.25** shows that the runner is experiencing a net negative impulse, and therefore must be losing velocity. In terms of the race, this might simply be due to

Figure 2.25: *Graph showing the horizontal ground reaction force acting on a sprinter for one footfall at the end of a 100 m race. The shaded area represents the impulse acting on the runner during foot contact with the ground.*

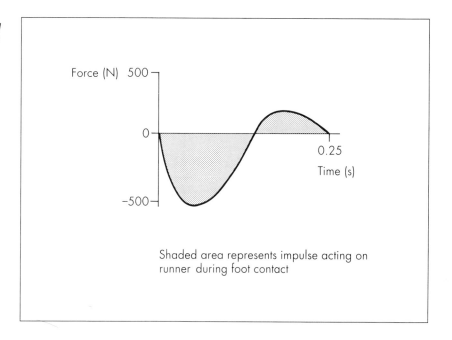

Shaded area represents impulse acting on runner during foot contact

fatigue, or a conscious effort on the part of the runner to 'ease up' before the tape.

❖ *Sports Mechanics Application*

Examination of horizontal force traces for high class sprinters shows that they tend to minimise the retarding forces and generate propulsive forces earlier in the contact phase. It has been suggested that this is achieved by the sprinters 'pulling' their foot onto the ground and under their body. This early phase of the contact may be more important than has been thought in the past. This is partly born out by the fact that the sprinters do not normally fully extend their leg in the 'push off' phase, but get into the recovery phase of the running cycle early

(Wood 1987)

So far the example of the sprinter has focussed on the horizontal ground reaction force. A brief consideration will now be given to the vertical ground reaction forces that are experienced during the run. It should be noted, that many of the principles applied to the vertical jump earlier in the text, are also appropriate to an analysis of the vertical component of the ground reaction force associated with sprinting.

During the analysis, it is vital to remember that when considering motion in a vertical plane, gravitational force as well as ground reaction force will determine any changes in motion.

At the start of the race, during the period from the starting gun to the feet leaving the blocks, the vertical ground reaction force will display a similar pattern to that of the horizontal ground reaction force. A typical pattern is shown in **Figure 2.26**

Figure 2.26: *Graph showing the vertical ground reaction force acting on a sprinter whilst in contact with the starting blocks. The shaded area represents the vertical ground reaction force impulse acting on the runner whilst in contact with the starting blocks.*

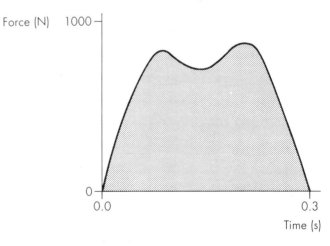

Shaded area represents the vertical ground reaction force
impulse acting on the runner when in contact with the starting blocks

The net vertical force acting on the runner *(taking into account the effects of gravity)* is shown in **Figure 2.27**.

Figure 2.27: *Graph showing the net vertical force acting on a sprinter whilst in contact with the starting blocks.*

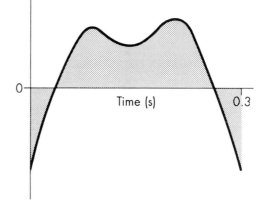

Having left the blocks, each footfall will evoke a vertical ground reaction force which has the pattern shown in **Figure 2.28**.

Figure 2.28: *Graph of the vertical ground reaction force of a single footfall during a 100 m race. The shaded area represents the vertical ground reaction force impulse acting on the runner during a single footfall when in contact with the track.*

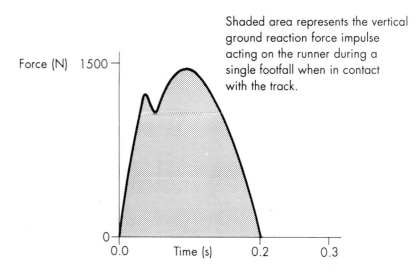

Unlike the horizontal ground reaction force, the vertical ground reaction force pattern will be little changed throughout the race. In fact, the pattern displayed in **Figure 2.28** is typical of traces produced by a wide variety of runners at a wide range of speeds. The first peak *(initial impact peak)* is sometimes smaller than shown in **Figure 2.28** and this is most frequently reported for runners who make contact with the ground with the front/mid part of the foot, *(the majority of runners that have been investigated make contact on the outside border in the middle/rear part of the foot)*. The length of time that the foot is in contact with the ground reduces as the runner's speed increases. In the example of the sprint race, the double peak pattern would almost certainly be retained throughout the race, but the base of the trace would become smaller as the speed of the runner increased.

The net vertical force acting on the runner during a single footfall is illustrated in **Figure 2.29.**

Figure 2.29: *Graph of the net vertical force acting during a single footfall in a 100 m race.*

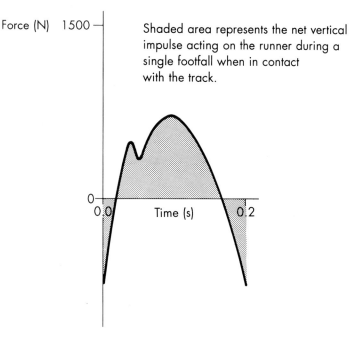

Shaded area represents the net vertical impulse acting on the runner during a single footfall when in contact with the track.

❖ *Sports Mechanics Application*

The initial 'spike' displayed in the vertical ground reaction force trace appears for most runners that are classified as rear foot strikers (that is the first contact of the foot is made with the rear third of the shoe). Because this peak force occurs very quickly at the start of the foot contact it has been suggested that it may be the cause of some running injuries. Running shoe manufacturers have designed shoes which attempt to provide cushioning from this shock. Even fairly modestly priced running shoes often show different materials and structure on the outside rear part of the shoe where the majority of rear foot strikers first make contact. Researchers investigating the cushioning effect report mixed results, but some indicate that the contact 'spike' often remains, even with increased cushioning.

(Miller 1990)

Figure 2.30: *Graph representing the impulse acting on the bowl during contact.*

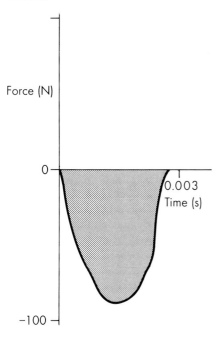

2.9 CONSERVATION OF LINEAR MOMENTUM

One of the implications of Newton's First Law is, that for any particular system of interest, unless a net external force is applied, the momentum within the system will remain constant. This is known as the **principle of conservation of linear momentum**, and holds true even when more than one object is defined in the system of interest.

For example in bowls it is sometimes necessary to 'fire' a wood *(bowl)* at another wood or the jack which is situated down the green. This involves the wood being played hard and straight in an attempt to collide with the 'target' bowl *(or jack)*. If the system of interest is defined to be the bowl plus the jack, then assuming influences such as friction and bias of the bowl to be negligible, then the the principle of conservation of linear momentum predicts that the amount of momentum before and after the collision will be the same.

After the bowl has been released, it has a certain quantity of linear momentum, and as the jack is stationary at this point, the entire linear momentum of the system of interest resides within the original bowl. *(The direction of the bowl's momentum is taken to be positive)*.

On contact with the jack the bowl applies a force to the jack, and in accordance with Newton's Third Law, the jack applies an equal but opposite force to the bowl. The contact forces on the bowl and the jack act for the period of time during which the two objects remain in contact. A graphical representation of these forces is shown in **Figures 2.30** and **2.31**.

It was noted in section 2.7, that a force acting over a period of time provides an impulse, which causes a change in momentum. It can be seen that the impulse experienced by the bowl and the jack was of exactly the same magnitude, but of opposite direction. Therefore both objects involved in the collision experience the same change in momentum, but in opposite directions.

In the case of the jack, this is observed as it gaining motion from its original stationary state *(that is an increase in its velocity)*. In the case of the bowl, it is observed to lose momentum *(as evidenced by a decrease in its velocity)*. As one object in the system has gained a given amount of momentum, and the other object has lost exactly the same amount, the total amount of momentum in the system of interest *(bowl plus jack)* is the same after the collision as it was before.

Note that the observed changes in speed of the two objects will not be the same unless they have the same mass. In this example the bowl would have a larger mass than the jack, and therefore its change in speed would be smaller than that of the jack.

The precise outcome for objects involved in collisions will depend on the masses of the objects involved, the velocity of the objects prior to the collision, and to a factor called the coefficient of restitution. This last factor is a measure of the elasticity of two objects.

Figure 2.31: *Graph representing the impulse acting on the jack during contact.*

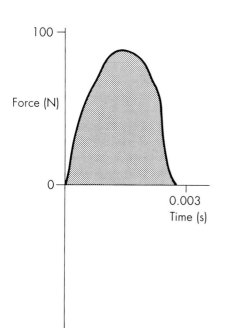

COLEG MENAI
BANGOR, GWYNEDD LL57 2T

2.10 FORCE AND MOTION RELATIONSHIPS

At this point in the text it is worth reflecting on some of the relationships between force and motion that have been identified so far.

In Chapter 1 *(sections 1.1 to 1.3)* when identifying quantities used to describe linear motion, it was noted that **displacement** can be derived from original position data ; and that **velocity** can be derived from displacement and time data; and that **acceleration** can be derived from velocity and time data. In this chapter it has been emphasised that it is **force** which causes an acceleration. A calculation which derives acceleration *(perhaps originally from simple position and time data)* can provide information about the force that was responsible for the original observed changes in motion. This would be an **indirect** method of obtaining information about the net force that was acting during the event under consideration.

However, it must equally be noted that the relationship can be expressed in opposite terms. If the force in a particular situation can be measured **directly**, then from the relationships that have been established, it can also be seen that the associated acceleration may be derived *(assuming the mass is known)*, and that the associated change in velocity can also be calculated, given time information, and finally that the associated displacement can be predicted.

It is this two way relationship which gives sport biomechanicians the potential to investigate and explain the causes of movements from original observations *(e.g., film and video)*, **or** to investigate and explain the movement outcomes resulting from measured force information *(e.g., force platforms)*.

SUMMARY

In this chapter the reader has been introduced to the following key ideas.

❖ The classification of forces into contact and non contact categories.

❖ The significance of describing a force as internal or external in a particular context.

❖ The principles associated with Newton's First Law of motion.

❖ The principles associated with Newton's Second Law of motion.

❖ The principles associated with Newton's Third Law of motion.

❖ The importance of accounting for all forces that are acting on an object.

❖ The principle of impulse and the associated impulse momentum relationship.

❖ Force components and their representation at an instant and over a period of time.

❖ Conservation of linear momentum.

Explaining Sport Performance

LINEAR MOTION

Part Two

OBJECTIVES

To enable the reader to understand the following.

❖ The principle of pressure.

❖ Factors determining friction.

❖ The principles that determine the flight characteristics of projectiles.

❖ The principles associated with the concepts of centre of gravity/centre of mass.

❖ The principles that determine the stability of an object.

❖ The concepts of work, energy and power.

3.1 PRESSURE

In many of the examples in the previous chapter, vector arrows were used to show the forces acting at one particular instant during a contact phase. When drawing these arrows, the base of the arrow should be positioned to represent the point of application of the force. However, it must be noted that when an object is in contact with another surface, only rarely would the contact be at a single point. More commonly, the contact would be between areas of the two objects involved in the interaction.

As the contact force is arising as a result of two areas coming together, then the concept of **pressure** needs to be understood.

The average pressure present in a contact situation is equal to the magnitude of the normal component of the force divided by the area of contact. The units for pressure are therefore newton per metres^2 (*newton metres $^{-2}$ or N·m^{-2})*

From the above description it can be seen that if the force remains constant, reducing the area of contact will increase the pressure.

For example, a gymnast performing a handstand, experiences a ground reaction force equal in magnitude to his/her weight, and this force is transmitted via the area of contact of the gymnast's hands with the floor. If the gymnast was to move from a two handed handstand to a one handed handstand, then the ground reaction force would remain the same in magnitude once the balance had been established, but would be acting over a smaller area and therefore the gymnast would experience a greater pressure on his/her hand.

If the vectors are now reconsidered, it can be noted that when the base of a vector arrow is drawn to show the point of application of a force, it should be drawn in a position which reflects in some way the pressure present at that moment. Potentially, this could be quite complex for events such as running, where the ground reaction force is varying along with the area of shoe in contact with the ground. Instruments such as a force platform which can be used for recording ground reaction forces can also produce a 'centre of pressure' value, which identifies an 'average' point to represent the point of application of the force.

In identifying a point of application in this way, the vector to be drawn can sometimes be positioned where there is no pressure at all! For example, for the gymnast performing a two handed hand stand, the 'centre of pressure' would be located in between the hands, where there is no contact at all.

3.2 FRICTION

Friction occurs whenever one surface moves or tries to move against another surface. In the example of the 100 m runner this would be the surface of the shoe and the surface of the track. The runner pushes against the track, and a friction force is generated, which may be considered to act on the runner in both side to side, and front to back directions.

One important characteristic of the interactions between surfaces is that the friction force opposes the intended motion *(of the foot/shoe in the case of the runner)*, and is equal to the component of the applied force which is parallel to the surfaces of contact, up to a particular critical value. Once the critical value has been reached, the magnitude of the friction force drops dramatically.

In the case of a runner, not using starting blocks, this could be illustrated when pushing hard against the ground. S/he might well find that his/her foot slips suddenly during the application of force. The value of the friction force immediately prior to slipping occurring is frequently known as **limiting friction**.

During the period of time when the surfaces are in contact, but moving relative to one another, the friction force is known as **sliding friction**.

There are two main factors which affect the magnitude of the friction force. Firstly there are the characteristics of the surfaces in contact. Sports shoes are designed with this in mind, and try to optimise the limiting friction for different surfaces and conditions e.g long and short studs, spikes in running shoes, soles for 'astroturf', etc.

It must be noted that optimal may not be maximal. In some sports events it is necessary that some slipping between the surfaces occurs so that the technique can be performed correctly, and/or that injury is not caused by a limb being too rigidly fixed. This is the case for many sports shoes. In sports where these factors are not significant, extreme measures are taken where the surfaces are actually fixed together as when cycle shoes are actually fixed to the pedals!

It should also be appreciated that in some sport situations, actions are taken to try to minimise frictional influences. Although the nature of frictional forces between skis and snow is considerably more complex than that described for running, it is frequently reported that different waxes are applied to the bottom of skis. The waxes used match different snow conditions, so that in downhill races, where the skis are kept flat to the surface of the snow, the friction due to snow/ski interactions is kept to a minimum.

The second factor which will determine the magnitude of limiting friction is usually referred to as the **normal force.** This is the force 'holding' the two surfaces together and is that component of a force that acts at right angles to the surface. The principle that applies with respect to friction, is that the larger the normal force then the larger the value of limiting friction. This relationship is frequently expressed in the following equation.

$$\mu_L = \frac{F}{R}$$

where:

μ_L = coefficient of friction *(limiting)*;

F = friction force at the point immediately prior to slipping;

R = normal force.

The value of μ_L remains constant for any two particular surfaces, and it can be seen that an increase in the normal force will be matched by a corresponding increase in the friction force, before slipping will occur.

A scrummaging machine standing on a level surface will have a normal force equal to its weight, and the rugby players will have to apply a force of a given magnitude parallel to the surface in order to reach the limiting friction point and start the scrummaging machine moving: **Figure 3.1.**

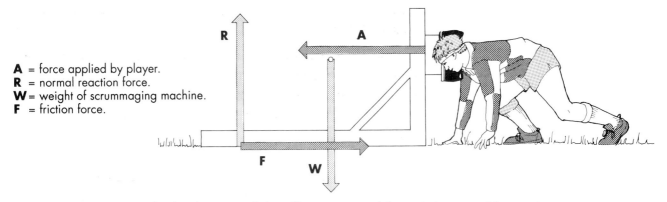

A = force applied by player.
R = normal reaction force.
W = weight of scrummaging machine.
F = friction force.

Figure 3.1: *Forces involved in the use of a scrummaging machine.*

If the effective normal force is increased by getting some additional players to stand on the scrummaging machine, then the players pushing must exert a proportionally larger force in order to start the machine moving: **Figure 3.2.**

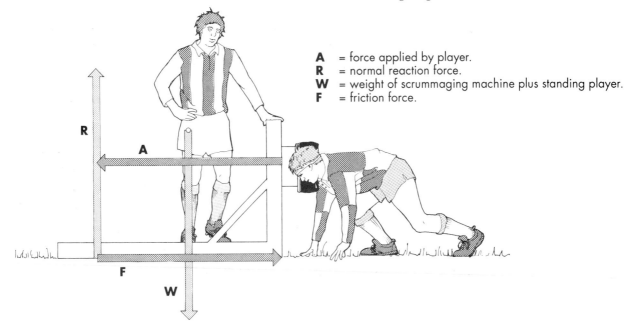

A = force applied by player.
R = normal reaction force.
W = weight of scrummaging machine plus standing player.
F = friction force.

Figure 3.2: *Forces involved in the use of a scrummaging machine with increased effective normal force.*

It is important to realise that as the normal force and the applied force *(and the associated friction force)* were increased by the same proportion, the coefficient of limiting friction remains the same in both situations.

❖ *Sports Mechanics Application*

An investigation conducted by Van Gheluwe and Depot (1992) looked at the surface friction forces exerted by tennis players when using an open stance and sideways movements in playing a forehand stroke. A variety of sports shoes and sports surfaces were tested. The experiment showed that the friction forces were more sensitive to changes in court surface than shoe. The result suggested that a player was unlikely to get an advantage in terms of 'grip' by using a particular type of shoe. The research also reported that results conducted on the shoe/surface combinations in laboratory conditions did not relate well to the results obtained in the 'field' situation.

3.3 PROJECTILES

This next section integrates much of the information that has been presented so far. Its foci are those activities which have a phase where the sportsperson or object is projected into the air. This includes events such as shot put, high jump, long jump, tennis, cricket, vaulting, etc.

Some of the principles considered in earlier sections are relevant to an analysis of projectiles. This should not be surprising, for if any force due to air resistance is ignored, then the only force that can contribute to an object's change of motion whilst it is in the air is gravitational force.

In an earlier example, **Table 2.1**, the flight phase of a ball thrown into the air was examined, and this represented a projectile's motion in a vertical direction only. Whilst there are a number of techniques that display the same vertical characteristics as the ball *(eg volleyball block, rugby lineout jump, basketball tip off, etc.)*, the rest of the section will devote itself to an examination of projectiles that are released at some angle to the horizontal.

Consider the example of the cricket outfielder who is returning the ball to the wicketkeeper without letting it bounce. The fielder imparts a large velocity prior to letting go, and the subsequent changes in motion of the ball can best be explained by considering the horizontal and vertical components of the ball's velocity after release.

If the horizontal velocity is considered first, it may be noted from the previous discussion of force, that if air resistance is considered negligible, then there are no other forces acting horizontally on the ball. The ball will therefore retain its initial horizontal motion

Figure 3.3: *Vertical and horizontal changes in velocity during the flight of a projectile.*

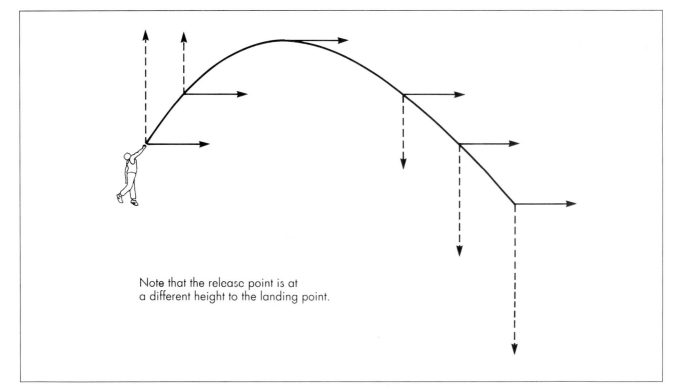

Note that the release point is at a different height to the landing point.

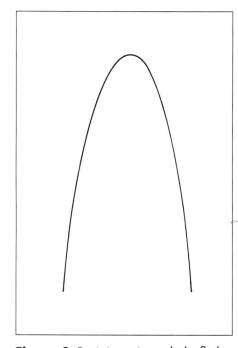

Figure 3.4: *A 'steep' parabolic flight trajectory.*

Figure 3.5: *A 'shallow' parabolic flight trajectory.*

unchanged until it is acted upon by another force. That is the horizontal velocity of the ball will remain constant until the ball hits the wicketkeeper's gloves.

The vertical velocity of the ball will be subject to exactly the same changes as were previously described for the ball that was thrown vertically. The only force acting vertically is gravity, and therefore the vertical component of velocity will be changing at the rate of − 9.8m·s^{-1} for every second that it is in the air. The effect of the change in vertical velocity, combined with the constant horizontal velocity is that the ball travels on a curved path called a parabola. The changes in the ball's component velocities are shown in **Figure 3.3**.

The precise shape of the parabola will be determined by the relationship between the magnitudes of the horizontal and vertical velocity components at release. A high vertical velocity component and a low horizontal component, will produce a high steep vertical parabola, as shown in **Figure 3.4**.

A low vertical velocity and high horizontal velocity will produce a shallow flat parabola as shown in **Figure 3.5**.

The relationship between the vertical and horizontal velocity components at release is defined by the angle at which the projectile is released. It should also be noted, that for a given speed of release, a projectile can travel the same horizontal distance *(range)* for two different angles of release. For example, a projectile released at an angle of 70° to the horizontal will travel the same horizontal distance as a projectile released with the same speed at 20°. The general principle for a given speed of release is that, two different angles of release which are equally displaced either side of 45°*(45 ± x°)*, will cause a projected object to travel the same horizontal distance, assuming that the take off and landing heights are at equal levels: **Figure 3.6**.

The points made above indicate that the cricket outfielder wishing to throw the ball to the wicket keeper, may throw the ball along a variety of different pathways, and provided that the wicketkeeper is in range, satisfy the requirement of accuracy *(that is, the ball ending up in the wicket keeper's hands)*. If, however, the fielder needs to get the ball to the wicketkeeper both accurately and quickly, then a low flat trajectory will be the most effective as the ball spends less time in the air.

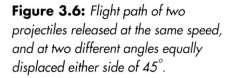

Figure 3.6: *Flight path of two projectiles released at the same speed, and at two different angles equally displaced either side of 45°.*

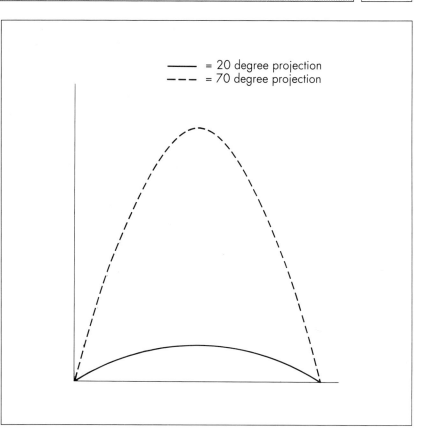

This last example serves to emphasise a number of important characteristics of projectiles. Firstly, it is the vertical component of the release velocity that largely determines the time that the projectile spends in the air. Secondly, it is the horizontal velocity at release that determines the horizontal distance that the projectile covers whilst it is in the air. This last point can be made clear if the basic equation for calculating velocity is considered.

$$\overline{v} = \frac{s}{t}$$

where:

$\overline{v}$ = velocity;

s = displacement;

t = time.

In the case of projectiles, the horizontal velocity may be considered to be constant throughout the flight phase *(if air resistance is considered negligible)*, and the time factor may be associated with the time in the air. If the formula is rearranged to make displacement *(range of the projectile)* the subject of the formula it can be seen that displacement is the product of the horizontal velocity and the time in the air.

$$s = v \times t$$

It is important to appreciate that the analysis just conducted uses the distinction between the concepts of speed and velocity that was emphasised in the previous chapter. In this case, it is essential to note that the term 'speed of release' only refers to how fast the object was travelling when it was released. 'Velocity of release' on the other hand implies both the speed of release and the direction of release *(which is usually defined as the angle of release)*. As the example of the cricket fielder indicated, two objects can have the same speed of release, but if they have different angles of release, they have different velocities of release. The vertical and horizontal velocities are the perpendicular components of the velocity of release, and as the example indicated, are major factors in determining how far a projectile will travel. In the case of a ball thrown at an angle of $70°$ with a given speed of release, the vertical velocity will be relatively high compared to the horizontal velocity. Therefore the ball spends a relatively long time in the air, but travels relatively slowly horizontally. Conversely, the ball that was released at an angle of $20°$ with the **same** speed had a relatively low vertical velocity. Therefore the ball spends a relatively short time in the air but travels relatively quickly horizontally.

3.3.1 PROJECTILE RANGE

In some sports events, the aim is to record the largest possible horizontal distance, e.g., long jump, shot and hammer. In such events the recorded value is made up from the horizontal distance the projectile travels in the air *(the projectile range)*, and other small horizontal distances such as the horizontal distance of the shot in front of the stop board at release. As the largest element of the recorded distance for these events will come from the projectile phase, it is important to understand the factors which will determine the projectile range.

If the example of a shot putter is considered these factors can be identified. A shot putter applies a force over a period of time to release the shot at a certain speed and angle. The question of 'What is the best angle?', immediately arises.

Figure 3.7: *Optimum angle of release for a projectile landing at the same height at which it was released.*

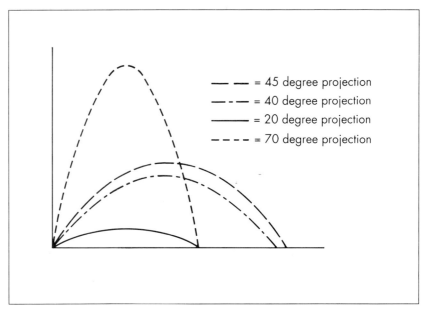

Figure 3.7 shows the predicted ranges for projectiles with the same release speed and different release angles. It would therefore appear from the diagram that the optimum angle of release for a maximum range is 45°. This is true for situations where the projectile is released and lands at the same height, but this is not the case for the shot, nor for many other situations in sport.

The theoretical optimum for the shot putter will be slightly less than 45°. The reason for this, is that the range is also dependent on the relative height of release. This is the difference between the height of release, and the height at which the projectile lands. The precise significance of this for the shot putter is shown in **Figure 3.8**.

Figure 3.8: *The optimum angle of release for a projectile landing lower than its release height.*

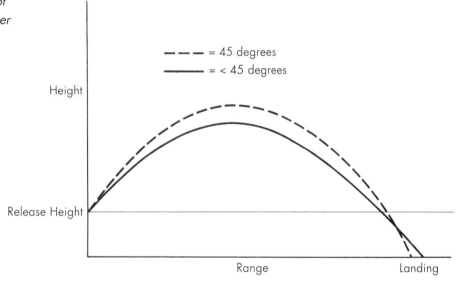

Observation of the diagram shows that when the different shot reach their release height on their downward path, the one that was released at less than 45° has not travelled as far as the one that was released at 45°. However, in the last phase of its flight, the shot released at the smaller angle 'overtakes' the shot that was released at 45°. The precise optimum angle for situations such as the one described above will depend on the relative height of release.

The principles outlined in this section are equally applicable to projectile situations where the athlete himself/herself is directly involved, as for example in the long jump.

❖ *Sports Mechanics Application*

An investigation, reported by Hay and Reid (1988), examined the relative importance of the factors determining a projectile's range. That is, the speed of release, angle of release, and relative height of release. Using real data, from a long jump, each of the three variables was systematically varied in turn by a constant proportion, whilst the other two were kept constant. The investigation found that an improvement/increase in each of the three variables, predicted an improvement in jumping performance. However, of the three variables, speed of release (take off) predicted the greatest improvements in jumping performance. This indicates, that a long jumper may well be wise to invest a greater proportion of the time spent in training concentrating on speed of take off.

When observing a multi-segment body such as that of a long jumper, the principles of projectiles are not so easily observed. It is therefore sometimes more convenient in mechanics to model the human body as a single particle.

The motion of such a particle is representative of the motion of the object as a whole. The next section considers the importance of this approach.

❖ *Sports Mechanics Application*

An investigation conducted by McDonald and Dapena (1991) compared the trajectory of the centre of gravity/centre of mass of elite male 110 m hurdlers and elite female 100 m hurdlers. The investigation reported that the centre of gravity/centre of mass reached the peak of its projectile flight directly over the top of the hurdles for the male hurdlers, but reached its peak 0.3 m before the top of the hurdle for the female athletes, who had a higher clearance over the top of the hurdle than the male athletes. Although at first sight it would appear that the female athletes could gain advantage by firstly, timing the take off so that the peak of the flight coincides with the top of the hurdle, and secondly by choosing a lower trajectory to reduce the time in the air, the researchers indicated that neither of these modifications would be advantageous. The reason for this is that a reduction in the time in the air would give insufficient time for the trail leg to be brought through, and a shallow parabola would bring the athlete in contact with the ground earlier which could upset the stride pattern between the hurdles. The researchers concluded that female hurdlers should not copy male hurdlers' technique.

3.4 CENTRE OF GRAVITY/CENTRE OF MASS

When the body is modelled as a particle then the terms used to identify the particle are **centre of gravity** or **centre of mass**. The motion of this theoretical particle will reflect the external forces acting on the body.

When Newton's Law of Gravitation, as specified below, is considered, it will be noted that the distance and masses referred to in the definition are relating to particles.

All particles attract one another with a force proportional to the product of their masses, and inversely proportional to the square of the distance between them.

In the case of the human body, it is the interaction between each particle making up the body, and each particle making up the earth, that results in the gravitational force. Specifically, it is the sum of the forces associated with the particles making up the body, that is referred to as the body's weight. Weight is a vector quantity and is shown as a force acting downwards towards the centre of the earth. The weight vector will have its point of application at the centre of gravity/centre of mass of the object.

One of the easiest ways of visualising the position of the centre of gravity/centre of mass is to recognize that it is the point of balance of the object. It is important to recognize that the point of balance will be the position where the net turning moment, due to the force of gravity, would be zero. This idea of there being a point about which turning moments of an object are zero, is often used as a way of defining the centre of gravity/centre of mass. If an object is suspended at a point, then the centre of gravity/centre of mass of the object, will lie along a line which is vertically below this point. This line is sometimes called a line of gravity

(NB. The turning moment of a force, is the twisting effect that a force has on an object. The concept of turning moments is explained fully in Chapter 5). A brief look at the diagrams in this text which show the weight of the object represented as a vector will show the point of application of this vector at the centre of gravity/centre of mass of the object/body in question.

The term centre of mass, is often used synonymously with centre of gravity, and the two points are often assumed to coincide. However, because the particles that constitute an object are not all equidistant from all the particles constituting the earth, then the gravitational force acting on each particle mass will differ very slightly. Whilst this means that the centre of gravity and the centre of mass will not coincide precisely, the difference between these two positions is so small that for the purpose of this text they may be considered to be identical.

Some examples may help to clarify the abstract nature of these points. In general, consideration of the distribution of an object's mass will give clues as to the location of the centre of gravity.

A shot, for example, has its mass symmetrically distributed about a central or middle point, and therefore the centre of gravity will be located at this point.

A cricket bat, on the other hand, will have more of its mass distributed towards the bottom of the bat, and so its centre of gravity will be towards that end.

(Notice that the centre of gravity of an object does not provide a

Figure 3.9: *Position of the centre of gravity for a wide variety of body positions adopted in gymnastic events.*

'boundary' which divides an object's mass or weight into equal 'halves' - it is the turning moments generated by the weight on either side of the centre of gravity, and not weight itself, which are equal and opposite.)

A hoop has its mass symmetrically positioned around a central point, but the central point actually occurs in the hole/space.

This last example serves to emphasise the abstract nature of the concept and also to highlight the fact that the centre of gravity need not lie within the actual mass of the object.

The examples quoted so far have been restricted to objects whose mass is 'fixed' in the sense of not being able to be redistributed. When considering situations which involve a sportsperson, the mass of the individual is not 'fixed' in this sense, and therefore neither is the centre of gravity.

Individual segments of the human body can be moved to an infinite variety of positions, and therefore the centre of gravity may also take up an infinite variety of positions. A person standing erect with arms by their side would have their centre of gravity at approximately the height of their navel, but by simply raising their arms above their heads, the centre of gravity would move in the direction of the arm movement.

Numerous techniques in sport involve the performer projecting themselves into the air, e.g. long jump, high jump, hurdles, and even running. In these events, it is the centre of gravity of the performer that will reflect projectile principles. It is important to note that in projectile examples, as the path of the centre of gravity is determined at take off, any movements of body segments while the jumper is in the air will not affect the centre of gravity's trajectory. In such circumstances, it is better to consider that segmental movements result in adjustments of the whole body position relative to the centre of gravity. This contrasts with the situation where the body is in contact with the ground, when segmental movements which are made result in movement of the centre of gravity relative to the ground, and in the same direction as the segmental movements.

High jump is an activity which illustrates well the usefulness of an understanding of centre of gravity in determining the potential effectiveness of techniques. In the following example it will be important to bear in mind the ideas associated with the concept of centre of gravity. Firstly, the idea that it is a point where the entire mass of the body can be considered to be located, and therefore that changes in the motion of the centre of gravity will in turn reflect changes in the motion of the athlete's body. Secondly, that the centre of gravity may be located outside of the actual matter making up a body.

When first learning to high jump, beginners frequently choose to use a technique called 'Scissors'. **Figure 3.10** shows an example of this technique for the position where the athlete is clearing the bar. Note especially the location of the centre of gravity of the athlete.

Figure 3.10: *The relative positions of the bar and centre of gravity of a high jumper (at the peak of flight) using a 'Scissor' technique.*

centre of gravity/centre of mass

As athletes become more advanced they may progress to the 'Fosbury flop'. **Figure 3.11** shows an example of the technique, again showing the clearance position.

Figure 3.11: *The relative positions of the bar and centre of gravity of a high jumper (at the peak of flight) using a 'Fosbury flop' technique.*

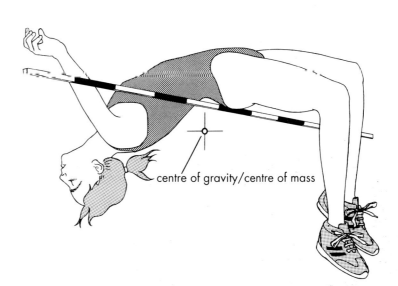

centre of gravity/centre of mass

If it is now assumed that **Figures 3.10** and **3.11** show athletes clearing a bar that has been set at the same height, it can be noted that the athlete performing the 'Scissors' techniques has had to raise his/her mass *(as reflected in the position of the centre of gravity)* much higher in order that the bar is cleared. In essence this means that the athlete using the 'Scissors' technique has had to generate a much larger vertical velocity at take off than the athlete using the 'Fosbury' technique in order to clear the bar.

One interesting feature of the 'Fosbury' technique is that it indicates that it is at least theoretically possible for the athlete's body to go over the bar whilst his/her centre of gravity passes underneath it! If this idea is examined it will be noted that this is a possibility because the centre of gravity may fall outside of the actual matter making up a body.

This idea would then suggest that a high jump technique, based on a body position where the centre of gravity was at its furthest from the body at the peak of the flight, would have considerable potential. Within this context, if an athlete could adopt a deep pike position at the peak of the flight, then a potential advantage could be gained. This has been called the Hay technique *(Hay 1978)*. In order to achieve this the athlete would have to use a run up which allowed him/her to approach the bar directly from the front. The requirement of a one foot take off means that the athlete would have to take off further away from the bar, than is possible in other techniques, in order that the non take off leg is accommodated. As a consequence it is unlikely that the athlete would be able to achieve the peak of flight directly over the bar, and therefore the potential advantage of the 'pike' technique is eliminated. Disabled athletes who have lost a leg use this technique very effectively as they are able to take off closer to the bar.

❖ Sports Mechanics Application

Basketball players when performing a jump shot are perceived to 'hang' in the air. Soccer players are also observed to use this technique when heading the ball. That is they maintain a level position at the peak of the flight. This observed 'hang' would at first sight appear to contradict the idea of a projectile following a parabolic flight. In an investigation of the basketball jump shot, Hay and Bishop (1979) traced the paths of the centre of gravity and a point on the jumper's head. The results showed that the centre of gravity followed the predicted parabolic path and that the head remained still at one level for approximately 0.2 s. The players were achieving this by precise timing of segmental movements, which causes the body to move relative to the centre of gravity position. One suggested advantage of the technique is that the basket ball could be released when the head of the player is relatively still. The disadvantage is that the player loses some of the vertical height that would have been achieved if the player had not adjusted his/her segmental positions in the air.

3.4.1 NET FORCE AND CENTRE OF GRAVITY/CENTRE OF MASS

The concept of the centre of gravity is not only helpful in explaining the principles of projectile motion associated with sports performers. Because the entire mass of a performer can be modelled as being concentrated at the centre of gravity, any net forces that are applied to the performer will result in the acceleration of the centre of gravity. This is a straight forward application of Newton's Second Law *(F = m × a)*, and this principle is used when changes in motion of a sports performer need to be recorded. For example, if an accurate measure of a sprinter's horizontal velocity or acceleration is needed, then it is the horizontal velocity or acceleration of the sprinter's centre of gravity that needs to be calculated. Examination of the sport mechanics applications included in this text will show how sport mechanics researchers have used this principle when describing different techniques in sport.

Figure 3.12: *Base of support in (a) a handstand; and (b) a headstand.*

a)

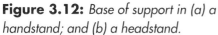

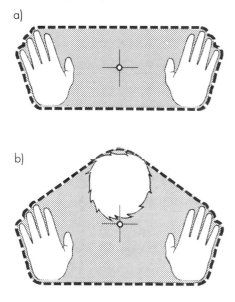

b)

Figure: 3.13: *Headstand with head in line with hands.*

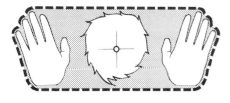

3.5 STABILITY

A brief mention is necessary of the concept of stability, which is closely related to some of the concepts associated with centre of gravity. For an object which is being supported by a fixed base, then the principles which determine stability are as follows.

The relationship between the position of the centre of gravity and the supporting base.
The base of support is defined by a line encapsulating both areas of contact and non-contact. In the case of a hand stand and headstand the supporting bases would be as shown in Figure 3.12.

Provided the centre of gravity lies over the supporting base then a stable position is maintained. However, as soon as the centre of gravity falls outside the limits of the supporting base then stability is lost. Moving the position of the centre of gravity so that it lies closer or further from the limits of the supporting base, varies the degree of stability. In balancing activities it will normally be the case that the centre of gravity is positioned away from the limits of the base in order to maximise stability. Note that in some balancing activities the limits of the base can be modified to help this aim. For example, in the headstand, by positioning the forehead in front of the hands, a triangular base is created, therefore making it easier for the gymnast to keep his/her centre of gravity within the support limits. Note that a beginning gymnast may place their head in line with their hands and thereby use a base which has no advantage over that used for a handstand *(see Figure 3.13)*.

In other situations the centre of gravity may be deliberately positioned in a non central position. For example if a judo player was anticipating receiving a blow from a certain direction, the centre of gravity might well be positioned close to the edge of the

Figure 3.14: *Stance of judo player anticipating a blow from the side with centre of gravity (a) at centre of supporting base, and (b) close to the edge of the supporting base nearest to the point of contact.*

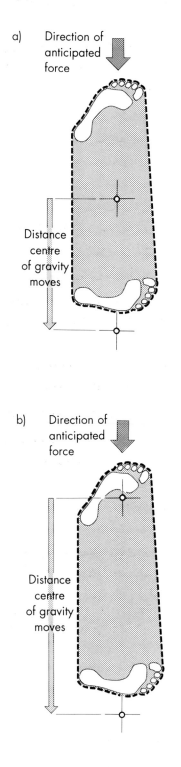

supporting base which is nearest to the point of contact. The advantage that the judo player may gain from this technique derives from the fact that the centre of gravity might have further to travel in the direction of the blow, before it fell outside the base. Therefore the judo player has a greater opportunity to retain his/her stability *(see figure 3.14).*

In yet other situations, a sports performer may deliberately use a position which is inherently unstable. For example a swimmer at the start of a race on the starting block may position his/her centre of gravity right at the limit of the support base, so that when the gun goes off, the very slightest push causes him/her to become unstable and therefore assist a fast start.

Height of centre of gravity above base

The principle here can be clearly observed in the stages of learning a headstand. Having established a good base of support, initially a gymnast may adopt a tucked position with the legs. This keeps the centre of gravity relatively low to the base. In later stages of the learning process the legs are straightened, thus causing the centre of gravity to move higher from the base. The second position is inherently more unstable than the first because the centre of gravity will fall outside the base of support after a relatively small angular displacement. In the first position, with the centre of gravity relatively low, the centre of gravity will have to experience a much larger angular displacement before an unstable position is reached, thus giving the beginner a bigger margin for error. In all sports where high degrees of stability are desired, a low centre of gravity position is advantageous.

The weight of the object

Increasing the weight of an object, potentially brings with it increased stability. In order for the centre of gravity to be moved outside of the supporting base, a turning force must be applied to the object. While the centre of gravity lies within the limits of the base of support, the weight of an object provides a force which contributes to resist the turning effect. The larger the weight, the larger the contribution to resisting the turning effect. However once the centre of gravity falls outside the limits of the base and stability is lost, then the weight of object only serves to increase the instability, until such time that a new stable position is adopted. Sumo wrestlers epitomise the importance of weight in assisting stability, but they also utilise the principles outlined in the previous two sections to enhance their performance.

3.6 WORK, ENERGY AND POWER

So far in the text, whenever force has been discussed with respect to changes in an object's motion, time has also been considered. Newton's Second Law has been expressed in terms of a force causing an object of fixed mass to accelerate *(which is based on a time rate of change)*, and also in terms of impulse causing a change in momentum, where impulse represents the effect of a force acting over a period of time.

The association of force with time is however not the only way of accounting for changes in motion. An alternative approach is to consider force acting over a distance, and in this context a force is described as having done some **work**.

The work done by a force on an object, is equal to the magnitude of the force multiplied by the distance the point of application of the force moves in the direction of the force.

This can be expressed as:

$$W = F \times d$$

where: W = work;

F = force;

d = distance point of application has moved in the direction of the force *(ie displacement)*.

Work is measured in newton metres *(N·m)*, or joules *(J)*.

Within the context of this definition, a javelin thrower does work on a javelin, a cricket bowler does work on a cricket ball, a weight lifter does work on a barbell, etc.

The work done on an object in changing an object's motion or position, is directly related to the amount of **energy** that an object has.

Energy may be defined as: **The capacity an object has to do work.**

In terms of understanding sports performance from a mechanical point of view, energy may be conveniently classified into two groups: **potential energy** and **kinetic energy**.

Potential energy is the energy an object possesses as a consequence of its position and/or its state.

An object's gravitational potential energy is the energy it possesses because of its position relative to a reference level such as the floor. The position of the object gives it the 'potential' to do work in falling to the reference level. The gravitational potential energy that an object possesses can be quantified using the following formulae:

$$PE = m \times g \times h$$

where: PE = potential energy;

m = mass;

g = acceleration due to gravity;

h = height above reference level.

The second category of potential energy is frequently referred to as **strain** or **elastic energy**. This is the energy that an object has when its shape is changed from its normal resting state. Examples include a ball in a compressed state, a trampoline that has been stretched, a bow string that has been extended, etc. In each of these situations the object has a 'potential' to restore itself to a neutral or normal resting state.

Kinetic energy is the energy which an object has because of its motion; both its linear and angular motion. An ice hockey puck travelling down the rink has linear motion, and therefore has linear kinetic energy. A high bar gymnast undertaking a grand circle has angular kinetic energy. A trampolinist bouncing and undertaking a somersault has both linear and angular kinetic energy.

The kinetic energy possessed by an object can be quantified using the following equations:

$$LKE = 1/2 \times m \times v^2$$

$$AKE = 1/2 \times I \times \omega^2$$

where:

LKE	=	linear kinetic energy;
AKE	=	angular kinetic energy;
m	=	mass;
v	=	linear velocity;
I	=	moment of inertia;
ω	=	angular velocity.

(moment of inertia and angular velocity are terms referring exclusively to angular motion and are considered in later chapters)

The unit for measuring energy is a **joule** *(J)*

The relationship between work and the various energy categories can be very complex. In order to aid an understanding of the relationship between work and energy, the following examples will ignore energy contributions associated with angular motion and strain/elastic events. The examples will also be used to introduce the concept of power.

In situations where the only force acting on an object is gravitational force, then the **principle of conservation of energy** can be observed.

Consider the example of the ball that is thrown vertically into the air without any spin. In this situation, at release, the ball has a certain quantity of linear kinetic energy and potential energy.

The kinetic energy is, in part, dependent upon its vertical velocity at release; and the potential energy at the same point will, in part, be determined by how far it is above the ground. If the energy of the ball is monitored during its flight, then in the upward path of its flight the ball will be losing kinetic energy, as its vertical velocity is being lost under the effects of gravity. At the same time as the ball is losing linear kinetic energy, it is gaining gravitational potential energy. At the peak of the flight, the ball will have zero linear kinetic energy, and maximum gravitational potential energy.

On the downward path of the flight the process is reversed. The ball now gains linear kinetic energy as its downward velocity increases, and at the same time it loses gravitational potential energy. If the ball is allowed to fall all the way to the ground, its gravitational potential energy will fall to a zero value, and its linear kinetic energy will reach its maximum, just prior to making contact with the ground.

Throughout the flight phase of the ball the total energy level of the ball remains constant.

It should be noted, that this conservation of energy principle should only be applied to situations in which gravity is the sole force acting on the object. This analysis can therefore be applied to sports situations where projectile motion *(ignoring air resistance)* can be used to describe and explain the performance.

Consider a second situation where a tennis server is throwing the ball into the air. In this example, the focus of attention is not the flight phase of the ball, but the phase immediately before it. In this phase, the server has the ball in his/her hand and is exerting an upward force on the ball, so that when it is released it travels to an appropriate height, in order to be struck by the tennis racket.

If certain assumptions are made with regard to the event it is possible to examine the so called work-energy relationship. This requires an appreciation of the amount of work the server does on the ball. It also requires an examination of the corresponding energy changes experienced by the ball.

The assumptions made are as follows.

a) The server applies a constant upward vertical force of 2.25 N during the throw.

b) The ball at the beginning of the throwing action was at rest *(in the server's hand)*, one metre above the floor.

c) The ball was released two metres above the ground.

d) The ball was released with a vertical velocity of 5 m·s⁻¹.

e) The mass of the ball was 0.1 kg.

f) The acceleration due to gravity is taken to be 10 m·s⁻².

Given these assumptions it is possible to confirm that the amount of work done on the ball by the server is equal to the change in energy experienced by the ball.

As it is known that a constant force of 2.25 N acted on the ball whilst its point of application was moved through a vertical distance of 1.0 m, according to the definition of work *(F × d)*, the total amount of work done on the ball by the server was 2.25 N × 1 m = 2.25 N·m or joules *(J)*.

The potential energy of the ball *(m × g × h)* was increased by a quantity equal to 0.1 kg × 10 m·s^{-2}×1.0 m. This is equal to 1 joule. *(Note that this is the **change** in gravitational potential energy compared to that in the original position).*

The linear kinetic energy *(½ × m × v^2)* of the ball was changed *(from zero)* to 0.5 × 0.1 kg × (5 m·s^{-1})^2. This gives a value of 1.25 joules.

Observation of the combined energy changes experienced by the ball reveals a total value of 2.25 joules, which is exactly equal to the work done on the ball. This confirms that the work done on the ball produces an equivalent change in the energy level of the ball.

In most of the examples cited above, the focus has been on sports implements rather than on the performer. It is however, possible to make the performer the focus. Because the performer, as explained in previous sections, has the capacity to vary the ground reaction force by accelerating body segments *(as a consequence of tensing and relaxing muscles)*, then it is possible to consider the work done by the ground reaction force on the performer. In order to consider this more fully it is necessary to introduce the concept of **power**.

Power is defined as **the rate of doing work, and is measured in units of work per unit of time e.g., joules·sec^{-1} or watts**; ie:

$$\text{Power} = \frac{\text{Work}}{\text{Time}}$$

Power relates the quantity of work that is done, to the time in which the work can be delivered. A quantity of work delivered over a short period of time would be described as a high power output, when compared to the same quantity of work delivered over a long time period.

The idea of being able to measure a sports performer's power output is an attractive one, as this might give coaches the ability to compare performer's potentials. However, it needs to be recognized that some sports activities require that work is done over a long period of time and others over a short period of time. In this sense it needs to be appreciated that particular methods of measuring power output may be more relevant to some events than others.

Sport scientists have tried to measure work and power in a variety of ways. In the following example, the power output *(and work done)* by an athlete performing a volleyball block, will be examined using information which can be derived from a force platform. This is a device which measures ground reaction forces.

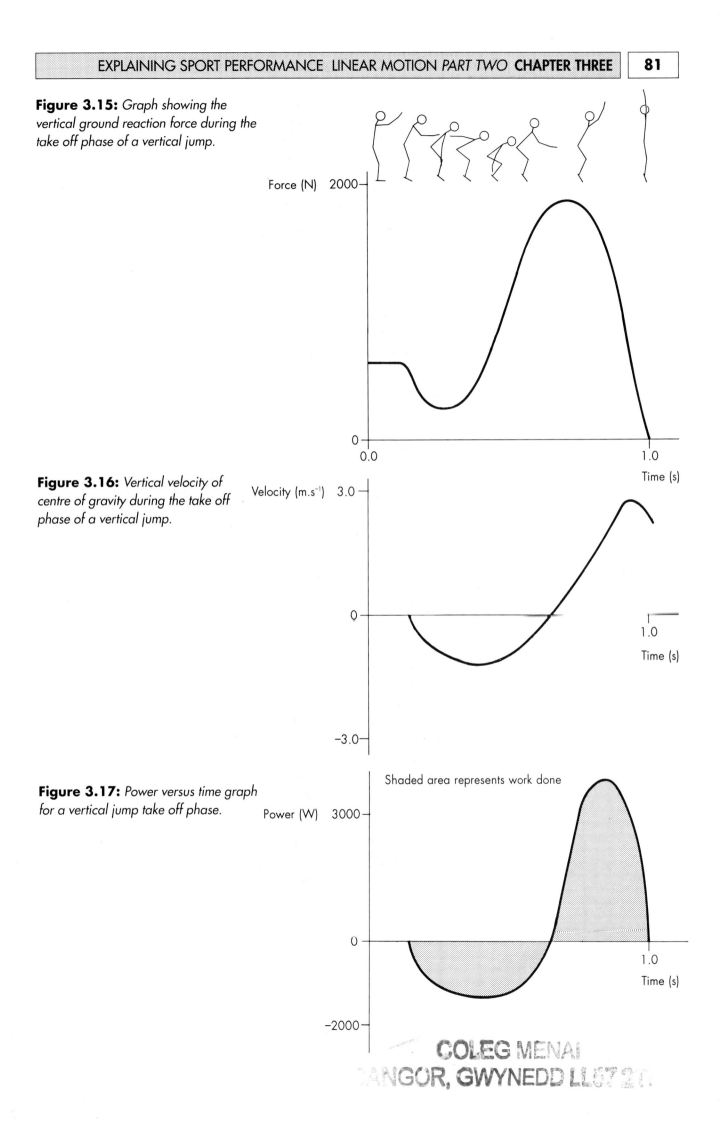

Figure 3.15: *Graph showing the vertical ground reaction force during the take off phase of a vertical jump.*

Force (N)

Figure 3.16: *Vertical velocity of centre of gravity during the take off phase of a vertical jump.*

Velocity (m.s⁻¹)

Figure 3.17: *Power versus time graph for a vertical jump take off phase.*

Power (W)

Shaded area represents work done

COLEG MENAI
BANGOR, GWYNEDD LL57 2

The technique used to examine power requires a rearrangement of the formula referred to earlier, as set out below:

$$\text{If Power} \ = \ \frac{\text{Work}}{\text{Time}}$$

Then $$P \ = \ \frac{F \times d}{t}$$

But as $\dfrac{d}{t}$ is defined as velocity:

$$P \ = \ F \times v$$

where: P = power;

F = force;

d = distance point of application moves in the direction of the applied force *(ie. displacement)*;

v = linear velocity;

t = time.

In an earlier section, it was noted that a vertical jump undertaken on a force platform would produce a ground reaction force like the one shown in **Figure 3.15**.

When the jumper's body is modelled as a particle *(centre of gravity)* then the vertical velocity curve for such an event would look like the one shown in **Figure 3.16**.

If the corresponding values of the vertical ground reaction force and vertical velocity curves are multiplied together *(F × v)*, then the resulting values give the power output of the jumper during the take off phase. The power versus time curve resulting from such a calculation would look like the one shown in **Figure 3.17**

It may be noted that as Power = Work/time, the area under the power versus time curve represents the work done by the jumper, that is:

$$\text{Work} \ = \ \text{Power} \times \text{Time}$$

Thus by summing the negative and positive areas represented on the power versus time curve, the net work done by the jumper can be estimated.

The negative and positive areas in the above analysis can be associated with different aspects of work. A negative area corresponds to what is called 'negative work', and positive areas with 'positive work'. In terms of the jumping activity, these different categories of work can be associated with the direction of the force and the direction of movement.

When the movement is in the same direction as the force, then positive work is being done. In this case when the jumper is moving upwards in the second half of the jump. When the movement is in the opposite direction to that of the force, then negative work is being done. This occurs in the first half of the jump, when the volleyball blocker is moving into the squat position prior to the forceful extension of hips and knees.

(It is worth noting that this analysis identifies eccentric muscle action with negative work, and concentric muscle action with positive work, e.g. quadriceps function during the jump, see 'Exercise Physiology' by C. Clegg, Feltham Press)

In making the above interpretations some cautionary observations need to be made.

Firstly, as it is a particle model of the human body that is being used, angular kinetic energy will not be accounted for.

Secondly, the calculation is unable to account for the contributions of any elastic energy changes due to the elasticity of various body tissues.

Thirdly, the definition of work makes reference to the 'point of application' moving in the direction of the applied force, but in a vertical jump the point of application of the ground reaction force is at the shoe/ground interface, and not at the centre of gravity whose displacement and velocity is actually used in any calculations.

The precise effect of these assumptions/issues on the calculations estimating total work done by the jumper is not clear. Alternative techniques which utilise film analysis and force platform data, attempt to resolve some of these problems by considering the energy changes within and between body segments. By summing these energy changes, the work done by the performer can be estimated.

SUMMARY

In this section of the text the reader has been introduced to the following key ideas.

❖ The concept of pressure.

❖ The concept of friction.

❖ The factors affecting the coefficient of friction.

❖ A projectile under the influence of gravity travels on a parabolic flight path.

❖The precise trajectory of a projectile under the influence of gravity will be determined by the speed of release, the angle of release, and the relative height of release.

❖ The vertical component velocity of a projectile changes under the influence of gravity.

❖ The horizontal component velocity of a projectile is constant *(in the absence of air resistance)*.

❖ The maximum range of a projectile released and landing at the same height is achieved with an angle of release equal to 45°.

❖ The maximum range of a projectile landing at a lower height than release is achieved with an angle of release less than 45°.

❖ An object with a distributed mass can be modelled as a theoretical particle called the centre of gravity/centre of mass.

❖ The changes in motion of the centre of gravity/centre of mass = will reflect the external forces acting on an object.

❖ Changes in the distribution of the mass of an object will be reflected in changes in position of the centre of gravity/centre of mass.

❖ The centre of gravity/centre of mass may be thought of as the point of balance of an object.

❖ The principle of stability is dependent on the location of the centre of gravity/centre of mass relative to the edge of the base area and its height above the supporting surface. The weight of an object also affects its stability.

❖ The concept of work and its relationship to force.

❖ The concept of energy.

❖ The classification of energy into kinetic and potential energy.

❖ The principle of conservation of energy.

❖ The concept of power.

The text so far has only dealt with situations which have not required an understanding of rotation. However, it must be appreciated, that in many sports events the essential movements are rotational in character, and that frequently the observed linear motion is itself underpinned by rotational motion. For example, in analysing a 100 m sprint it is important to appreciate that it is the underlying rotational motion of the body segments that result in the linear displacement of the runner when viewed as a single object.

It is therefore important that the mechanical principles associated with angular motion are identified and explained. Many of the concepts to be considered in the next section have direct parallels with the linear situations already discussed.

4

DESCRIBING SPORT PERFORMANCE
ANGULAR MOTION

OBJECTIVES:

To enable the reader to understand the following.

❖ The concepts of angular distance and angular displacement.

❖ The concepts of angular speed and angular velocity.

❖ The concept of angular acceleration.

❖ How to interpret graphical representations of angular motion.

❖ How to calculate angular velocity and angular acceleration using numerical techniques.

INTRODUCTION

Linear motion can be described by using specific mechanical motion descriptors, and the same is true for angular quantities. Similarly, just as linear motion descriptors could be classified as vector and scalar quantities, so can angular motion. However, it must be stated at the start of this section, that the representation of angular vector quantities by using arrows is considerably more complex than for the linear case.

The principle that needs to be recognized is that angular vectors have a magnitude and direction just like their linear counterparts but, in the case of angular vectors the direction characteristic is defined by the direction of the axis of rotation. More specifically, it is the direction which is determined by the 'right hand rule'.

To apply the right hand rule the fingers are curled to represent the direction of rotation, and the thumb is straightened. It is the direction of the thumb that indicates the direction of the axis of rotation. For a rotation therefore, that was taking place in an anticlockwise direction in the plane of the paper (*as you are looking at it*), the vector would be directed out of the page towards you: **Figure 4.1**. A vector representation of this angular motion would therefore be an arrow, which was directed out of

Figure 4.1: *Demonstration of the 'right hand rule'.*

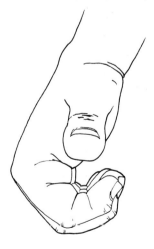

the page, and whose length was proportional to the magnitude of the quantity being represented.

Detailed manipulation of angular vectors in a three dimensional context is beyond the scope of this text. Therefore, examples of angular motion will be restricted to motion which can be considered to take place in a single plane. To help interpretations of data, anti-clockwise rotation will be regarded as positive, and clockwise rotation as negative.

4.1 ANGULAR DISTANCE AND ANGULAR DISPLACEMENT

One basic question which is frequently asked when wishing to describe motion is 'How far has the object moved?' In the case of angular motion this is answered with reference to the angle that the object has moved through, between chosen starting and finishing positions.

In the angular context, the description is made either with reference to **angular distance**, or to **angular displacement** The distinction between these two parameters can best be made by considering an example.

A golfer prepares to hit a ball off the tee with the club vertical to the ground as shown in **Figure 4.2**.

The golfer then takes the club away from the ball until it arrives at the top of the backswing, pointing directly at the intended direction of travel of the golf ball, and having been taken through an angle of 270° as shown in **Figure 4.3**.

The angular distance for this motion would be described as a rotation of 270°, but an angular displacement would be described as 90° in a clockwise direction. In other words, the angular displacement attributed to a rotating object is always the smallest angle between the starting and finishing position being considered.

Where the angle between the starting and finishing position is less than 180° and there has been no change in the original direction of motion, then the magnitudes of angular distance and angular displacement are the same: **Figure 4.4**.

The units for angular distance and angular displacement are either degrees, or radians. The latter units are frequently required for calculations where angular parameters are combined with other measurement parameters. One radian is equal to 57.3°.

The reader should also note, that although the distinction between angular distance and angular displacement has been made on the basis of direction, that angular displacement is not in fact a vector quantity.

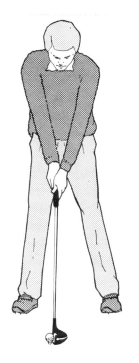

Figure 4.2: *Starting position of golfer preparing to hit a ball off the tee.*

Figure 4.3: *Finishing position of golfer at the top of the backswing.*

Figure 4.4: *Two club positions where the angle between the starting and finishing position is less than 180°.*

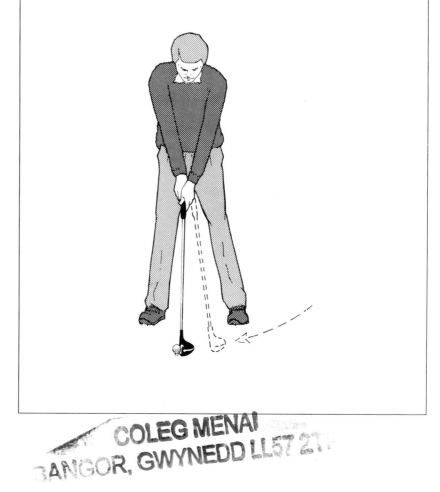

COLEG MENAI
BANGOR, GWYNEDD LL57 2T

❖ *Sports Mechanics Application*

An investigation by Kollath and Scwintz (1988) considered the difference in soccer throw-in techniques when players threw from a standing position as compared to a throw with a run up. The investigation recorded the angular position of joints of the body at various stages in the movements, but failed to find any common patterns which correlate with the longest throws.

For all subjects, longer distances were recorded for the run up technique. Other factors that were found to correlate significantly with the distance of the throw, were the velocity of the ball at release and the velocity of approach (run up). The majority of throwers were recorded as releasing the ball at an angle below the optimum that theory would predict. The investigators suggested that this might be poor technique, or be related to tactical factors. That is the increased time in the air which would result from a higher release angle might be tactically undesirable.

4.2 ANGULAR SPEED AND ANGULAR VELOCITY

In Chapter 1 *(section 1.2)* describing linear motion, the parameters of speed and velocity were identified as measures of the rate of change of distance/displacement. In the same way **angular speed**, and **angular velocity** perform the same quantification function for rotational motion. These two parameters are derived as follows:

$$\text{angular speed} = \frac{\text{angular distance}}{\text{time}}$$

$$\text{angular velocity} = \frac{\text{angular displacement}}{\text{time}}$$

Observation of these formulae reveal the close parallel with the equivalent definitions for linear motion.

Under the conventions outlined earlier, the units for these two parameters are either degrees per second ($°·s^{-1}$), or radians per second ($rad·s^{-1}$).

When analysing angular motion such as a golf swing, a sport biomechanician would frequently take a high speed film record of the events, for example 200 frames per second.

The angular motion would then be analysed on the basis of successive frames. With this kind of analysis two adjacent frames would record the angular displacement over a very small time period, for example $1/200$ second, and therefore the angular velocity for that time period could be calculated.

This is the average angular velocity for that time period. However, it should be recalled from the earlier discussion, that when time periods get very small, the measures calculated more closely represent an instantaneous value.

As angular velocity values can be calculated for each time interval *(between successive frames)*, then a 'picture' can be built up for the angular velocity over the whole period of the event. This 'picture' is often represented as a graph.

The raw angular data in the following example have been taken from an analysis of a runner on a treadmill. The data represent the successive angular positions of the upper leg *(hip to knee segment)* of the runner during one complete running stride. That is, from the right foot making contact, back to the same position at the next foot fall.

The data is taken from a video record running at an equivalent of 25 frames per second. The runner was running at a constant 6 m·s⁻¹. The conventions of angle measurement are shown in **Figure 4.5**.

The stages in calculating the angular velocity of the upper leg are shown in **Table 4.1**.

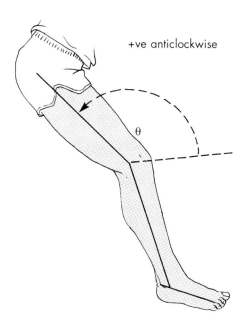

+ve anticlockwise

θ

Figure 4.5: *Angle measurement convention for upper leg.*

Table 4.1: *Stages in calculating the angular velocity of the upper leg.*

T (s)	Upper L (deg) Position	Dis (deg)	ω (deg·s⁻¹)	Point in Cycle
0.00	148.3			Foot contact.
		−4.6	−115.0	
0.04	143.7			
		−8.0	−200.0	
0.08	135.7			
		−12.0	−300.0	
0.12	123.7			
		−5.8	−145.0	
0.16	117.9			
		−14.9	−372.5	
0.20	103.0			Foot off
		−25.7	−642.5	
0.24	77.3			
		−21.2	−530.0	
0.28	56.1			
		0.0	0.0	
0.32	56.1			
		8.6	215.0	
0.36	64.7			
		12.6	315.0	
0.40	77.3			
		22.3	557.5	
0.44	99.6			
		24.1	602.5	
0.48	123.7			
		21.2	530.0	
0.52	144.			
		2.3	57.5	
0.56	147.2			

The graph showing variation in angular position for the right upper leg during a running cycle can now be drawn and is shown in **Figure 4.6**.

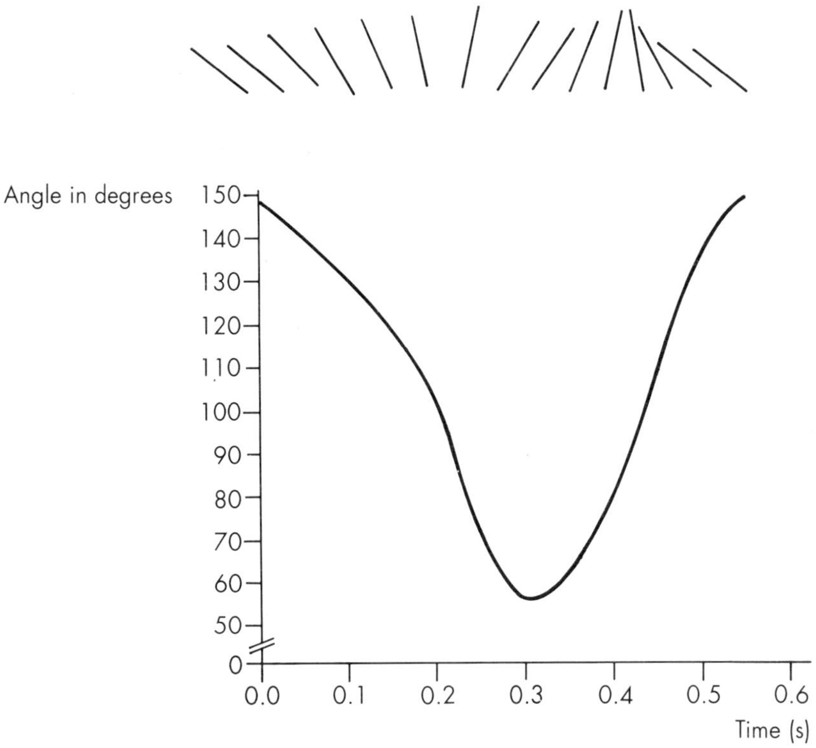

Figure 4.6: *Graph showing variation in angular position for the right upper leg during a running cycle.*

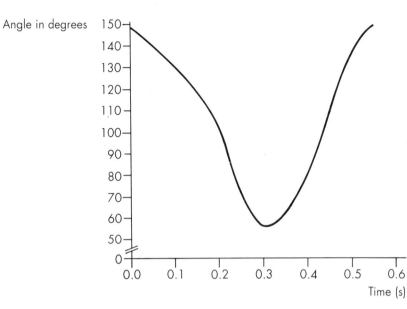

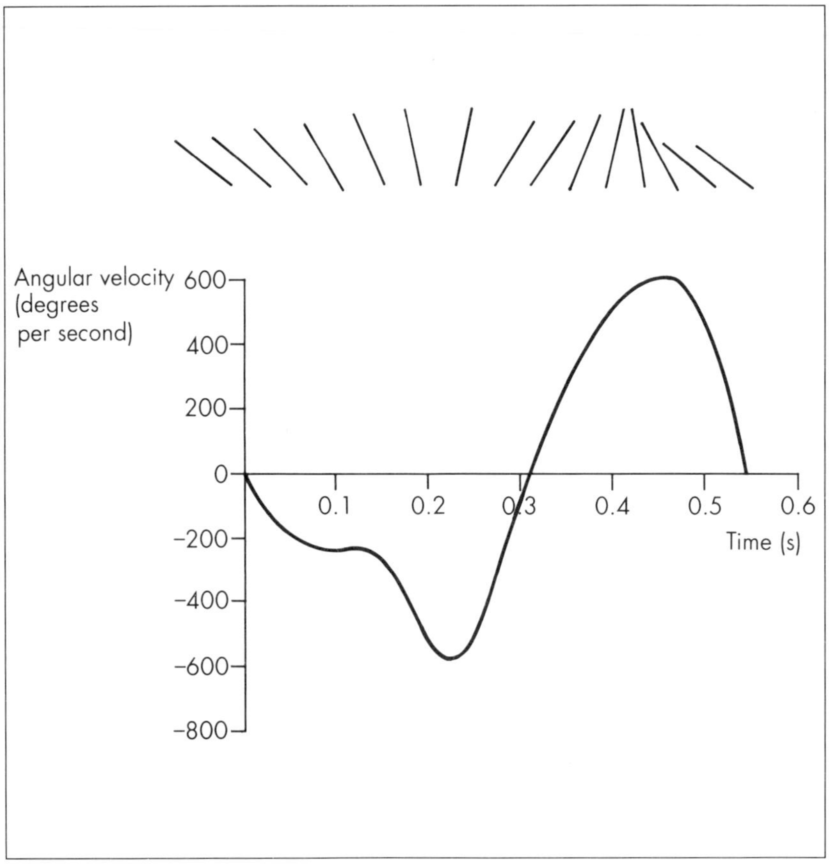

Figure 4.7: *Angular velocity of upper leg versus time.*

It may be recalled, that in Chapter 1 *(section 1.7)*, it was explained that an instantaneous value for speed could be obtained by considering the gradient of a distance versus time graph.

In the same way, the tangent procedure explained previously, could be used to calculate the gradient of an angular position versus time graph. This would reveal information about instantaneous angular speed. In the case of angular motion which can be assumed to take place in a single plane, then whether the gradient is positive or negative, will give information about whether the angular velocity is positive or negative, that is the direction of the angular motion.

For the data provided, the tangent method would not really be appropriate, as the time intervals being used are fairly small, and detailed information about angular positions for the end points of these time intervals is available. Plotting the calculated values, from **Table 4.1**, for angular velocities, gives the graph shown in **Figure 4.7**.

4.3 ANGULAR ACCELERATION

The last quantity in this section to be considered is **angular acceleration**. This may be defined as the rate of change of angular velocity, and can be written as a formula in the following terms:

$$\text{angular acceleration} = \frac{\text{change in angular velocity}}{\text{time}}$$

or

$$\overline{\alpha} = \frac{\omega_f - \omega_i}{t}$$

where:

$\overline{\alpha}$ = average angular acceleration;

ω_f = angular velocity at the end of the time interval;

ω_i = angular velocity at the start of the time interval;

t = time interval.

The units of angular acceleration are either degrees per second per second *(deg·s^{-2})*, or radians per second per second *(rad·s^{-2})*.

In the example of angular data for the runner's upper leg, the table could have been extended, so that an additional column could include the changes in the recorded angular velocities for each time interval. Dividing by the time interval value would then have given an angular acceleration column. This information could then be plotted on a graph. In practice, care has to be taken in interpreting angular acceleration values derived in this way, as the process of finding differences accentuates any errors in the original data.

❖ *Sports Mechanics Application*

An investigation by Lees and Aitchison (1983) compared the angular motion of the upper and lower leg of skilled and non skilled rugby place kickers. The results showed the skilled kickers did not generate a higher angular velocity of the lower leg than the non skilled kickers, but that for the skilled kickers the maximum angular velocity occurred closer to the point of contact with the ball. This suggests that the skilled kickers were timing the kick more effectively. The results for the upper leg showed that the skilled kickers had a positive angular velocity at contact whilst the non skilled kickers had a negative angular velocity (that is it had changed direction). This indicates that the skilled kickers were 'driving through' the ball and therefore lends support to the idea that the 'follow through' is an important element in kicking technique.

SUMMARY

In this section of the text the reader has been introduced to the following key ideas.

❖ The principles of angular distance and angular displacement,

❖ The principles of angular speed and angular velocity,

❖ The principle of angular acceleration.

❖ The numerical procedures for calculating angular motion descriptors.

5 EXPLAINING SPORT PERFORMANCE
ANGULAR MOTION

OBJECTIVES:

To enable the reader to understand the following.

❖ The principles associated with the concepts of Torque/Moments.

❖ The principles of levers.

❖ The principles associated with Newton's First Law of motion as applied to angular motion.

❖ The principles associated with Newton's Second Law of motion as applied to angular motion.

❖ The principles associated with Newton's Third Law of motion as applied to angular motion.

INTRODUCTION

It has been explained in Chapter 2 *(section 2.4)* that when an external force is applied to an object which is not in any way restrained, the object will experience a linear acceleration. It may now be noted that, if the external force is applied in such a way that its line of action does not pass through the centre of gravity of the object, then, in addition to a change in its linear motion, the object will also experience a change in its angular motion.

A force which acts 'off centre' is called an eccentric force. The twisting or turning effect produced by an off centre force is called the **moment** of the force or **torque**.

An object that is not restrained will therefore experience a change in its linear motion and its angular motion.

If the object in question is actually restrained from moving along its linear path because it has a fixed axis, or has a point in contact with a fixed surface, then the change in rotational motion can be explained by identifying the force which is 'off centre' to the axis or point of contact.

When trying to explain the effects of such off centre forces in sport situations, it is important to recognize that the 'objects' experiencing the force may be simple in their basic structure, or very complex as in the case of the sports performer. Because of this complexity, in some cases it is reasonable to assume that the 'object' will behave like a single rigid object, in other cases, and in particular when dealing with the actual performer, alternative models have to be used because this assumption is unrealistic.

5.1 TORQUE/MOMENTS

The moment of a force *(or torque)* may be defined in the following way.

The moment of a force *(or torque)* is equal to the magnitude of the force multiplied by the perpendicular distance between the line of action of the force and the axis/pivot.

From this definition it may be noted that the turning effect can be changed by manipulating:

a) the magnitude of the force;

b) the perpendicular distance from the axis to the line of action of the force; or,

c) both of these factors.

The units of measurement for torque are newton metres (N·m).

It is important to remember that it is the perpendicular distance that is important. This perpendicular distance between the pivot and the line of action of the force is frequently termed the 'moment arm'. Diagrams in the rest of the chapter illustrate moment arms in a variety of situations.

5.1.1 NET TORQUE

In the same way that the notion of net force was stressed as being important in understanding observed changes in linear motion, so the notion of a net moment or net torque is vital to an understanding of changes in angular motion. Where two or more moments are acting on an object, it is the combined turning effect that is responsible for any change in angular motion experienced by the object. The precise relationship between an applied torque and the change in an object's angular motion is discussed in section 5.5.

Figure 5.1: *Some diagrams showing the generation of moments of force (torque) - F × d.*

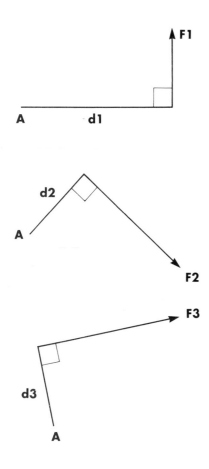

A = Axis or pivot
F = Force
d = Perpendicular distance from line of action of force and pivot.

5.2 LEVERS

The lever approach to understanding moments and torque is valuable when the object of investigation can be modelled as a rigid beam, and where a fixed pivot/axis can be clearly identified.

Lever systems are most often used to explain rotational motion in situations where the forces acting on a system can be functionally identified as effort forces, and resistive forces. That is, forces which are acting primarily to generate rotation in a required direction *(effort forces)*, and forces that generate torques which are opposing the desired direction.

The actual effectiveness of the lever system will depend on the relationship between the effort force, resistive force, and the pivot. The relationship between these factors is frequently used as a means of categorising levers into one of three classes.

5.2.1 FIRST CLASS LEVERS

A first class lever is one where the pivot lies between the resistive and effort forces as shown in **Figure 5.2**.

An example of a first class lever can be seen in rowing machines where the 'oar' is the rigid object which is pivoted at the rowlock. In this situation the effort force is applied by the rower, and the resistive force arises as a result of the machine generating a torque via springs or similar devices: **Figure 5.3**.

Figure 5.2: *First Class Lever.*

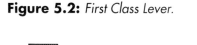
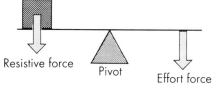

Figure 5.3: *First Class Lever system in a rowing machine*

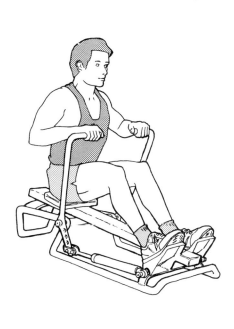

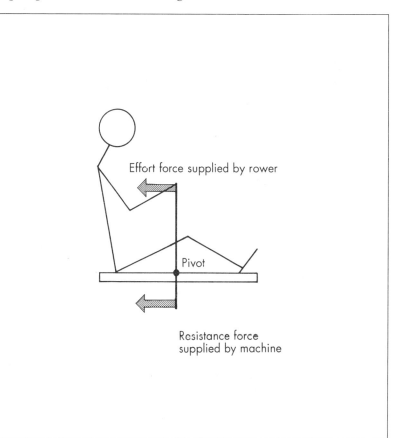

Figure 5.4: *Second Class Lever.*

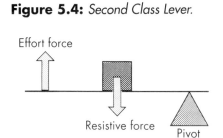

5.2.2 SECOND CLASS LEVERS

A second class lever is one where the resistive force lies between the pivot and the effort force: **Figure 5.4**.

Figure 5.5 shows an example of a second class lever in action during a weight training session. The athlete is undertaking an exercise designed to train knee extension. An upward force is applied by the athlete on a beam with a fixed pivot. The resistance is provided by weights attached to the beam.

Figure 5.5: *The application of a Second Class Lever in a piece of weight training apparatus.*

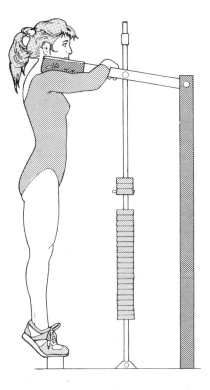

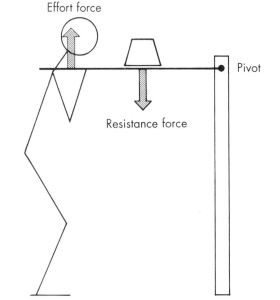

5.2.3 THIRD CLASS LEVERS

A Third Class Lever is one where the effort force lies between the resistive force and the pivot: **Figure 5.6**.

Figure 5.7 shows a lacrosse player about to throw the ball. The pivot is assumed to be at the bottom of the stick, which is held by one hand, and the effort force is provided by the other arm. The resistive force in this case is a combination of the lacrosse stick's weight and the weight of the ball.

Figure 5.6: *Third Class Lever.*

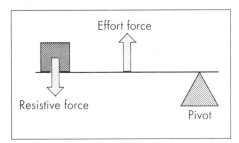

Figure 5.7: *A Third Class Lever in a Lacrosse Throw.*

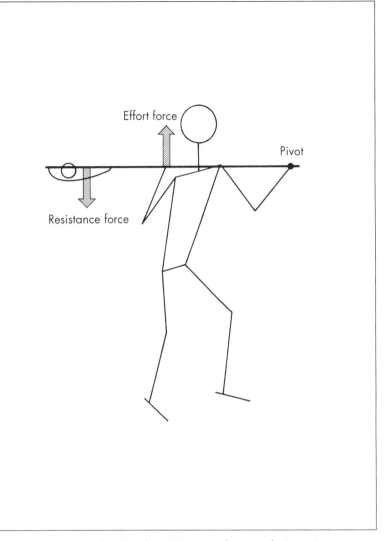

It is necessary to emphasise that it is not always obvious into which lever class a particular situation should be placed, as it depends on how the action of forces is perceived.

The functional value of a lever system can be described in terms of whether its overall design helps to magnify the effects of the effort force, or to increase the speed of movement experienced by a particular point on the lever.

The main functional attributes for each of the lever classes can be summarised as follows.

First Class Levers:
where the pivot is nearer the point of application of the effort force, the lever will emphasise the speed of movement;

where the pivot is nearer the point of application of the resistive force, the lever system will magnify the effects of effort force.

Second Class Levers:
magnify the effect of the effort force.

Third Class Levers:
emphasise the speed of movement of the lever.

5.3 ROTATION GENERATION IN SPORTS PERFORMANCE

It was noted earlier, that explaining rotation generation in the context of a sports performer, can be complex. The following section looks at rotation generation in a variety of situations where the sports performer is the focus of interest.

5.3.1 SUPPORT/CONTACT SITUATIONS

In some situations, the axis is a fixed one, and the performer can reasonably be modelled as a single rigid object. In such situations the torque generating force may be considered to be the weight of the performer. This force acts off centre to the fixed axis. This is the case for a gymnast in the initial phase of a grand circle on the high bar as shown in **Figure 5.8**. Provided the gymnast remains in a rigid position, the moment arm associated with the force will change as the performer moves around the bar. Therefore the magnitude of the torque will be constantly changing

Figure 5.8: *The weight of a gymnast acting as a torque generating force with respect to an axis acting through the bar.*

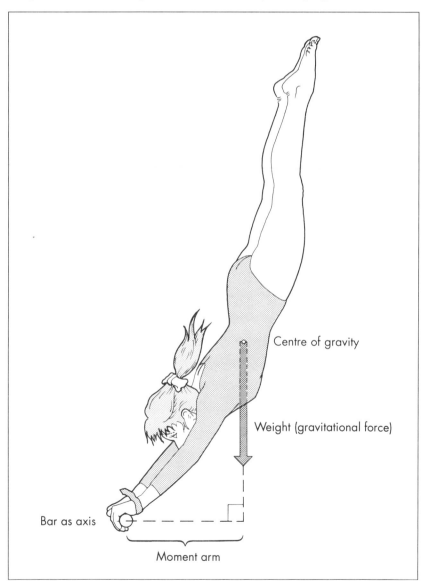

Centre of gravity

Weight (gravitational force)

Bar as axis

Moment arm

In other situations, because the object in question is free to move *(not physically attached)*, the axis is not so easily identified.

If the situation involves an athlete in contact with a fixed support surface, and body segments are kept in a fixed position relative to one another *(that is the body is kept rigid)*, then the axis of rotation may be considered to pass through the point of contact. A diver in the initial toppling phase of a high board dive may display these characteristics: **Figure 5.9**. As in the case of the high bar gymnast, the torque generating force during the toppling phase may be considered to be the weight of the diver.

Figure 5.9: *The weight of a diver acting as a torque generating force with respect to an axis passing through the point of contact.*

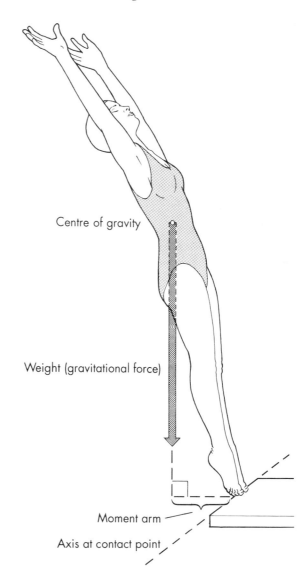

Centre of gravity

Weight (gravitational force)

Moment arm

Axis at contact point

Events where the body can reasonably be considered to be a single rigid object are rare. A more common situation occurs where individual body segments are accelerating, while a performer is in contact with a support surface.

Segments will be rotating about a number of joint axes, but a single 'axis' needs to be identified and also an external off-centre force.

In order to understand the principles of rotation generation as applied to the whole body during such a phase, the single 'axis' should be considered to pass through the centre of gravity of the sportsperson.

From the previous discussion of centre of gravity, it should be apparent that, as the body segments are moving relative to one another, the centre of gravity of the sportsperson, and thus the 'axis', will constantly be changing its position during such a contact phase.

The off-centre force in these situations is provided by the ground reaction force. As was noted in Chapter 2 *(section 2.6)*, the ground reaction force will vary in magnitude and direction, in a direct relationship with the changing motion of the body segments. This means that the magnitude of the torque being generated is constantly changing.

Figure 5.10 shows a gymnast during the take off phase for a move which requires backwards rotation. The diagram shows the relationship between the ground reaction force and the centre of gravity at one particular instant. If such a relationship is maintained over a period of time then it will generate both rotation and linear motion in the gymnast.

Figure 5.10: *Ground reaction acting as a torque generating force with respect to an axis passing through a gymnast's centre of gravity.*

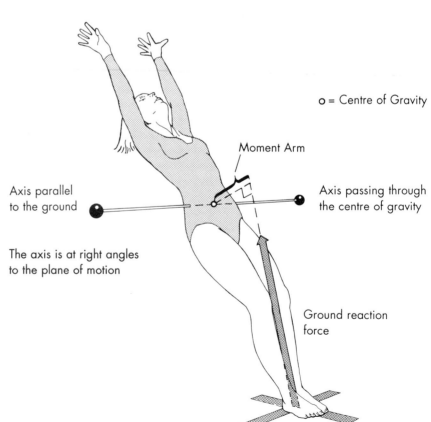

o = Centre of Gravity

Moment Arm

Axis parallel
to the ground

Axis passing through
the centre of gravity

The axis is at right angles
to the plane of motion

Ground reaction
force

5.3.2 NON SUPPORT SITUATIONS

Consider now an object that has been projected into the air. It will be recalled from an earlier analysis, that the centre of gravity of that object will travel in a parabolic curve *(assuming negligible air resistance)*, and that the path of the centre of gravity is fixed once the object is released *(or freed from any contact)*. If the object is rotating on release, it may be noted that for the period of time the object is in the flight phase, this rotation will take place about an axis which passes through the centre of gravity.

This would be the case whether the object in question was a discus, or a gymnast performing a somersault, or indeed any other situation where the object has been projected. It is even true for objects such as boomerangs whose centre of gravity may lie outside the actual matter which constitutes them. Thus a gymnast performing a piked somersault will rotate about an axis which passes through his/her centre of gravity, and this may fall outside the actual mass of the gymnast.

It should be noted that during a somersault, even though the gymnast may change his/her body position during the flight phase *(and therefore segments may rotate about a variety of joint axes)*, the axis of rotation for the whole body will always pass through the centre of gravity. It may also be noted that whilst in the air, the only external force affecting the gymnast is the force of gravity *(ignoring any effects due to air resistance)*. This force may be considered to act through the gymnast's centre of gravity and therefore is not acting off-centre to the axis: **Figure 5.11.**

Figure 5.11: *The weight of a diver acting through the axis of rotation during a non support phase.*

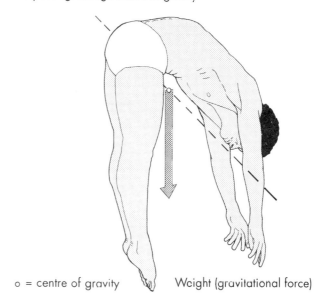

Axis passing through centre of gravity

o = centre of gravity   Weight (gravitational force)

The relationship between torque and changes in angular motion is examined more fully in the next section, with a consideration of Newton's laws.

5.4 NEWTON'S FIRST LAW - ANGULAR ANALOGUE.

The First Law may be stated as follows.

An object will continue to rotate with a constant angular momentum unless acted upon by a net external torque.

Frequently this law is summarised as the principle of conservation of angular momentum.

This definition introduces a new concept of **angular momentum**.

Angular momentum may be considered as the measure which quantifies the amount of angular motion that a particular object possesses.

It may be recalled that in the linear context, momentum was defined in terms of an inertial parameter, and a rate of change of displacement parameter. Specifically, linear momentum was defined as mass × velocity. Angular momentum is similarly based on an inertial parameter, and a velocity parameter.

The inertial parameter must reflect an object's reluctance to change its state of rotational motion. In the linear context it was observed that it was the object's mass that determined this 'reluctance to change'. For objects which possess angular motion, the mass of the object alone is not sufficient to account for the reluctance an object displays to any potential change in its angular motion. A complete account of rotational inertia needs to consider the mass of the object, and how that mass is distributed relative to the axis of rotation.

Consider the example of the trampolinist who is to perform a somersault. On taking off, the trampolinist has a certain amount of angular motion. According to Newton's First Law, unless s/he experiences a net external torque, the amount of angular motion *(angular momentum)* will remain constant.

A person watching the trampolinist, would observe that at some point during the move the trampolinist would tuck up, and in association with this tucking action, the trampolinist would rotate faster.

At first sight it might appear that the trampolinist has increased the amount of rotation *(angular momentum)* that s/he possesses. For this to be true, the gymnast would have to have experienced a net external torque. However, if the influence of air resistance is ignored, then during the flight phase the only external force that the trampolinist experienced was the force of gravity.

It was noted in Chapter 3 *(section 3.4)* that the force of gravity for an object may be considered to act at the centre of gravity. It has also been noted that the axis of rotation for a gymnast during a flight phase would also pass through the centre of gravity. Under these circumstances, the force may be considered to act through the axis, and therefore is not 'off-centre'. Gravity therefore cannot, according to Newton's First Law, be increasing the amount of rotation *(angular momentum)* that the gymnast possesses, as there is no external torque acting on the trampolinist.

Given that the trampolinist has a fixed amount of rotation, but is observed to rotate faster when s/he tucks, this indicates that the 'reluctance' *(inertial value)* must have been reduced. This is exactly the case for the trampolinist, and the characteristics of the inertial properties for rotational motion can now be summarised as follows.

Where the mass of an object is distributed away from the axis of rotation the inertial value will be relatively large.

Where the mass of an object is distributed close to the axis of rotation then the inertial value is relatively small.

The name given to the the inertial parameter for angular motion is **moment of inertia.** This characteristic can be changed by a sportsperson altering the position of his/her body segments relative to the axis of rotation. It should be noted that this is unlike the inertial characteristic for linear motion, which can only be changed by increasing, or decreasing, the mass of the object.

The units for moment of inertia are **kg·m²** which reflect the mass and distribution characteristics of the parameter.

From the above examples it may be noted that angular momentum, which defines the quantity of angular motion possessed by an object, may be expressed in the following terms:

Angular Momentum = Moment of Inertia × Angular Velocity.

(Units for angular momentum = $kg \cdot m^2 \cdot s^{-1}$)

Consideration of this formula shows that if angular momentum remains constant, as was the case for the flight phase of the trampolinist, then any adjustment in the value of moment of inertia, must be accompanied by a reciprocal change in the angular velocity. So not only will the trampolinist rotate more quickly when s/he tucks, but conversely the rate of rotation will reduce when a stretched position is adopted prior to landing.

The concept of angular velocity when applied to a multi-linked object like the human body is not always easy to appreciate, particularly where the individual links themselves are not rigid or of fixed mass. If a rigid link model is assumed *(see Figure 2.8)*, then if the links remain in a fixed orientation to one another, the angular velocity of any segment will reflect the angular velocity of the body. In situations where the angular velocity of individual segments is different, which is in the majority of situations, then an **approximate** value for the body can be obtained by considering the angular velocity of the head-trunk segment.

A diagram indicating the relationship between moment of inertia and angular velocity during the flight phase of a back somersault is shown in **Figure 5.12**.

Figure 5.12: *The relationship between moment of inertia and angular velocity in a standing back somersault (flight phase).*

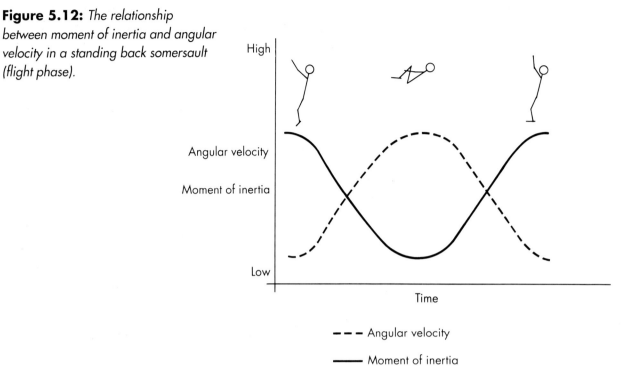

It was noted earlier in this section that the key concepts of Newton's First Law are embedded in the principle of the conservation of angular momentum. The following account emphasises another important feature of this principle.

It may be recalled from previous discussion that if a long jumper is considered as the system of interest, then it is not possible for this system to gain or lose any angular momentum whilst it is in the air *(if air resistance is assumed to be negligible)*. The long jumper will therefore have any angular momentum that exists at take off until s/he is back in contact with the ground.

Whilst a long jumper has no particular need for rotational motion, the take off technique almost inevitably generates some forward rotation. Because the forward rotation will tend to rotate the jumper's body into a poor landing position the long jumper tries to control this rotation.

Some jumpers employ techniques, such as the 'sail', which partly rely on keeping their moment of inertia high, therefore reducing the angular velocity and the negative effects of the rotational motion. Other jumpers employ the hitch kick technique which utilises the conservation of angular momentum principle.

The hitch kick is a complex technique involving upper and lower body segment rotations. As the angular momentum of the jumper's body *(the system of interest)* is constant during the flight phase, any angular momentum which arises as the result of a segmental rotation *(which is initiated during the flight phase)* must be **internal** to the system. Given that the total angular momentum in the system must remain constant, some adjustment in the angular momentum in another segment must occur in order to maintain the system's overall total.

The 'unwanted' forward rotation gained by the jumper at take off can therefore be 'taken up' by segmental rotations which are in the same direction as the 'unwanted' rotation.

The principle is best observed in the **forward** cycling arm motion of the hitch kick technique. *(The legs are also involved but the technique is a little more complex)*. The net effect of the arm and leg segmental rotations is to reduce the rotation of the trunk. As it is the hips of the jumper that have a prime role in determining the position of the legs at landing *(the further forward they are at landing the better)*, it is in the jumper's interest to restrict forward rotation of the trunk as much as possible.

It must be noted that if the jumper stops the segmental rotations prior to landing then the 'unwanted' forward rotation of the trunk will again be evident. However, if this occurs at the very end of the jump, then there may be the potential to rotate the body past the landing position of the feet and so be of some benefit to the jumper.

Before concluding this discussion it is important to emphasise that all rotating objects will have rotational inertia. Even when a potential for changing angular momentum does exist, that is when external torque is present, the observed outcome of such a change will reflect the existing moment of inertia at the time. One example of this which is frequently cited is the recovery phase of a runner's leg.

If the axis of rotation is considered to pass through the runner's hip, then flexing the knee will bring the mass of the lower leg closer to the axis of rotation, thus reducing the moment of inertia of the leg about this axis. For a given torque applied by the runner's hip flexor muscles to the leg during the recovery phase, a more rapid change in the angular velocity *(acceleration)* of the leg is observed when the knee is flexed to its full extent, compared to when it is only flexed a little.

The fact that the leg can be brought through more quickly may be of little consequence to the middle or long distance runner, but for the sprinter it is highly significant. Hence one common technique practiced by sprinters is to 'kick their heels close to their backside' during the first half of the recovery phase of the stride.

5.5 NEWTON'S SECOND LAW - ANGULAR ANALOGUE

Newton's Second Law may be stated as follows.

The rate of change of angular momentum experienced by an object is proportional to the external torque causing it, and the change occurs in the direction of the applied torque.

This can be expressed as a formula in the following way:

$$\overline{L} = \frac{(I_f \times \omega_f) - (I_i \times \omega_i)}{t}$$

where:

$\overline{L}$ = average applied torque;

I_f = moment of inertia at end of time interval;

I_i = moment of inertia at start of time interval;

ω_f = angular velocity at end of time interval;

ω_i = angular velocity at start of time interval;

t = time interval..

If the moment of inertia does not change then the equation can be re-written as:

$$\overline{L} = I \times \alpha \quad \textit{(where } \alpha = \textit{angular acceleration).}$$

This formula is less useful than its linear equivalent *(F = m × a)*, and in practice a further rearrangement of the form shown below is frequently more helpful in explanations of human movement situations.

$$\overline{L} \times t = (I_f \times \omega_f) - (I_i \times \omega_i)$$

In this form, the left hand side of the equation may be termed **angular impulse**, and the right hand side 'change in angular momentum'. *(Note that angular impulse equals torque × time)*. It should be noted that in numerical work using the above formulae, the angular velocity and angular acceleration must be expressed in units of radians·s^{-1} and radians·s^{-2} respectively.

Consider the example of a gymnast performing a flick-flack from a stationary starting position. **Figure 5.13** shows the forces acting on the gymnast at one particular instant during the take off phase. The forces shown are the ground reaction force and the gravitational force.

In accordance with the description of the generation of rotation given in section 5.3, it is the ground reaction force that should be considered as generating a torque. By collecting this torque data for the whole period of the take off, it is possible to draw a torque versus time graph, and an example is shown in **Figure 5.14**.

Inspection of the graph in **Figure 5.14** shows that the area under the graph represents torque × time, or angular impulse. As angular

Figure 5.13: *Ground reaction force generating a moment (torque) about an axis passing through the centre of gravity during the take off phase of a flick flack.*

Note that the diagram shows the situation at one precise instant in time.

o = Centre of Gravity

Axis parallel to the ground

Axis

d

F = Ground reaction force
d = Perpendicular distance between line of action of the ground reaction force and the centre of gravity *(axis).*

Weight

F

The axis is at right angles to the plane of motion

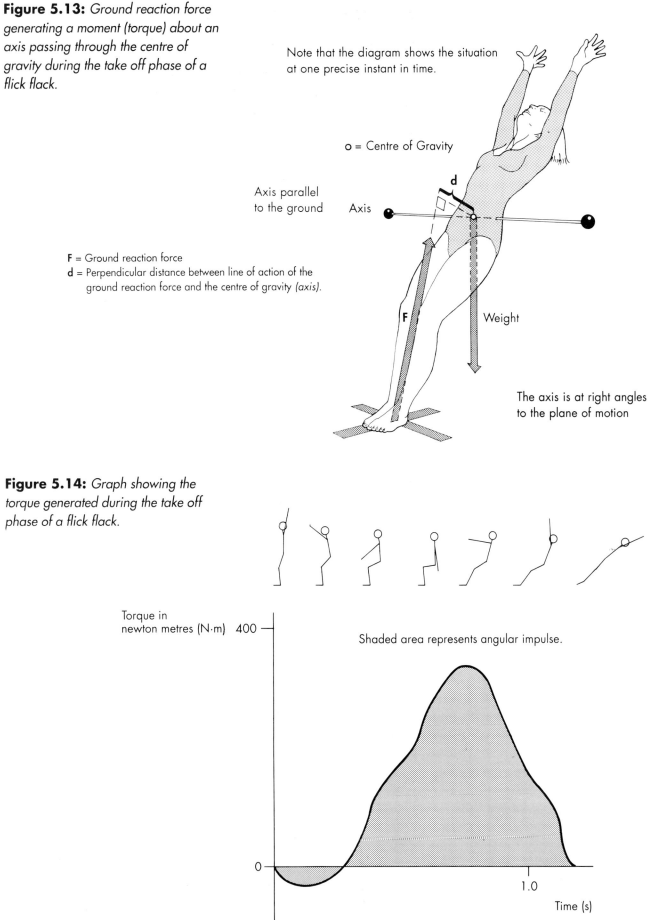

Figure 5.14: *Graph showing the torque generated during the take off phase of a flick flack.*

Torque in newton metres (N·m) 400

Shaded area represents angular impulse.

0

1.0

Time (s)

-100

impulse has been shown to cause a change in angular momentum, then the area under the curve also represents the change in angular momentum experienced by the gymnast.

In this case the gymnast started with zero angular momentum, and therefore the change in angular momentum will reflect the total angular momentum possessed by the gymnast at the point of take off.

❖ *Sports Mechanics Application*

Sanders and Wilson (1987) investigated the angular momentum requirement for a one and half forward somersault dive with and without a single twist. The results showed that, for the individuals investigated, the techniques with twist required 6–19% more angular momentum.

Hwang I et al (1987) investigated the angular momentum in double layout and double tucked somersaults. The results showed that considerably more angular momentum was required to successfully complete the layout somersaults. This result supports the mechanical theory and endorses the use of tucked, to piked, to layout, as learning progressions in somersaulting based techniques.

One further example may help to clarify the concepts discussed here. Gymnasts when performing a floor exercise, are frequently observed in their diagonal tumble run to perform several flick flacks in sequence, and then end with a double somersault. The reason for the series of flick flacks is that it enables the gymnasts to gradually build up their angular momentum, so that when they take off for the double somersault they have sufficient angular momentum to enable them to complete two rotations.

It should be emphasised that, as was explained in an earlier example, the gymnast cannot gain any angular momentum in any of the flight phases between flick-flacks, or in the final double somersault flight phase. Therefore, if insufficient angular momentum has been built up in the preliminary tumble run, even if the gymnast tucks fully *(which will increase his/her angular velocity)*, the gymnast will be unable to complete the move successfully.

5.6 NEWTON'S THIRD LAW - ANGULAR ANALOGUE

Newton's Third Law may be expressed as follows.

For every torque exerted by one object on a second object there is an equal but opposite torque exerted by the second object on the first.

The discussion of the Third Law in a linear context emphasised the simultaneous nature of the action-reaction forces, and the same is true for torque in the angular context.

The law is well illustrated by the pike jump often performed by beginners on the trampoline: **Figure 5.15**.

Figure 5.15: *Position of body before and after a pike action.*

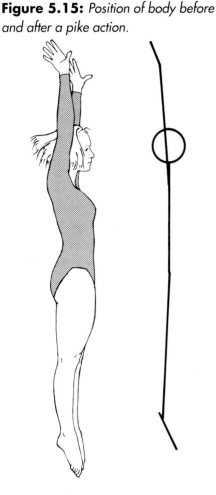

Lower 'half' of body moves through a greater range of movement than upper 'half'
Angle **A** is less than angle **B**

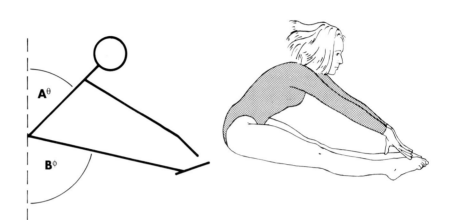

In this case the two 'objects' in question are the upper and lower halves of the trampolinist's body. In performing the pike, an equal but opposite torque, provided by the gymnast's muscles, is applied to each half of the body. If it is assumed that the two halves of the body were not rotating at the onset of the torque application, then they will rotate in opposite directions, one clockwise and the other anti-clockwise, relative to their original starting position.

It should be noted that although the two halves of the body experience exactly the same magnitude of torque, for exactly the same period of time, the actual observed range of movement *(rotation)* may be different. The reason for this can be identified by considering the principle of moment of inertia outlined earlier.

The different objects *(in this case the two halves of the body)*, each have different moments of inertia, and therefore they will experience different angular accelerations $(\overline{L} = I \times \alpha)$. This in turn means they will experience different changes in angular velocities, and travel through different angular displacements, during the time the torque is acting.

Where the two objects are a sportsperson and the planet, the effect on the planet is not observable. In watching a high diver jump and twist from the board, the effect of the torque applied from the board on the diver is immediately apparent, but the effect on the board *(and hence the planet)* of the equal but opposite torque applied by the diver is not seen.

SUMMARY

In this section of the text the reader has been introduced to the following key ideas.

❖ The key components making up a lever system.

❖ The three class classification of levers.

❖ The functional advantages and disadvantages of lever systems.

❖ The identification of axes of rotation in situations of rotation generation

❖ The principles of torque and moments.

❖ Newton's First Law for angular motion.

❖ Newton's Second Law for angular motion.

❖ Newton's Third Law for angular motion

EXPLAINING SPORT PERFORMANCE
FLUID FORCES

OBJECTIVES:

To enable the reader to understand the following.

❖ The nature of interactions with fluid environments.

❖ The principles of drag and lift forces in air environments.

❖ The effects of spin on objects in an air environment.

❖ The effects of drag and lift forces on swimming performance.

❖ The principle of the buoyant force.

At the beginning of Chapter 2 it was noted that forces arise as the result of interactions. So far in the text, the forces which arise as the result of objects interacting with fluid environments, have been assumed to be insignificant.

This chapter will outline some of the issues which need to be considered for situations in sport where such interactions are likely to be of importance.

6.1 FLUID ENVIRONMENTS

A fluid environment within the context of sports events can be thought of as one where movement takes place in air, in water, or in a combination of these. Therefore a shuttlecock when it has been hit, has its movement modified by forces associated with its interaction with air; a scuba diver has his/her movement modified as the result of interacting with a water environment; and a sailing yacht's movement is determined by its interaction with both water and air environments.

The precise nature of the force experienced by the object is dependent on a variety of factors, and these are identified in the following section. As the examples in this text have focussed on activities which take place in an air environment, it is these situations that will be mainly used to illustrate fluid mechanics principles. Only a brief account will be given of the interactions in a water environment.

6.2 INTERACTIONS IN AN AIR ENVIRONMENT

The forces acting on an object in an air environment can initially be categorised as drag forces, and lift forces. These concepts can best be understood by considering some basic principles.

6.2.1 VELOCITY OF FLOW AND PRESSURE DIFFERENCES

A sports ball moving very slowly through the air will cause the air to flow smoothly around the ball as shown in **Figure 6.1**. This is known as laminar flow.

Figure 6.1: *Smooth (laminar) flow around a ball moving relatively slowly through the air.*

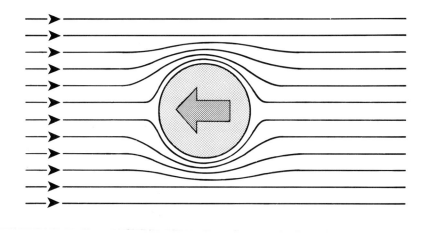

It makes no difference whether one considers that the ball is stationary and the fluid is flowing past it, or the reverse situation, where essentially the fluid is stationary and the ball is moving through it. The relative velocity in these two situations is the same

Notice in **Figure 6.1** that lines *(known as stream lines)*, representing the pattern of flow, appear to be closer together as they pass around the ball. At these points, the air will be being compressed and travelling faster than at the front or back of the ball, where the stream lines are wider apart.

The fact that the air is travelling faster at some points of the flow, than at others, is significant. According to a principle called the **Bernoulli effect**, fast flowing fluid will exhibit low pressure characteristics, and slow moving fluid will exhibit high pressure characteristics.

This principle can be easily demonstrated by holding a flimsy strip of paper in front of your mouth and blowing across the top of it, thus creating a high velocity flow of air which has low pressure.

Because the top surface of the paper has a low pressure area compared to the underside of the paper, there is a force acting in an upward direction as the air attempts to restore a pressure balance. As you blow, the paper moves **up** towards the area of low pressure/high velocity air. Where there is a pressure difference such as this, it is referred to as a 'pressure gradient'.

If the diagram of the ball is considered once again, it will be seen that the air flow characteristics are symmetrical on either side of the ball. Because of this, the net forces acting on the ball are zero. Therefore no changes in the ball's motion would be expected.

As the air travels around the ball, the layer directly in contact with the ball's surface is slowed down by surface friction, which is also known as **surface drag.** Adjacent layers of air will also experience a consequent effect of the surface friction, and they in turn will be slowed down. In general, surface drag can be reduced, by making the surface smoother. The layer of air immediately next to the ball is called the **boundary layer.** It is the behaviour of the boundary layer and adjacent layers which frequently determine the forces experienced by the ball.

Figure 6.2: *Air flow around a fast moving ball.*

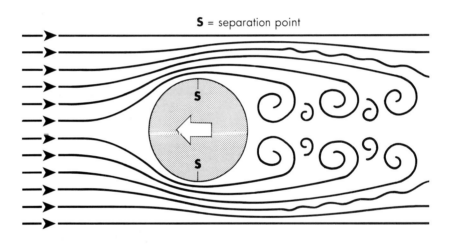

In the example of the ball, if it is now assumed that the ball is travelling faster, then the diagram representing this situation would look like the one shown in **Figure 6.2**.

In this diagram, the air flowing around the ball has been unable to follow the surface of the ball, and has broken away to form fast moving eddies of air. When the air no longer flows smoothly it is called **turbulent flow.** Because the fast moving air at the back of the ball has a relatively low pressure compared to the air at the front of the ball, there is a pressure difference which results in a force acting on the ball in a direction from front to back *(this may be considered as suction acting on the ball)*. This force is frequently called **profile** or **form drag.** If the air breaks away from the surface of the ball near to the leading edge of the ball there will be a greater quantity of form drag.

6.2.2 FACTORS AFFECTING DRAG

Form drag is dependent upon the relative velocity of the ball and air, the cross sectional area of the ball, and the shape and surface characteristics of the ball, that is how streamlined the ball is.

Variations in these factors will cause changes in the drag force that the ball experiences. Particularly critical is the velocity of the ball, as a doubling of the velocity will result in a quadrupling of the drag force. This squared relationship exists within a defined range of circumstances, and then the behaviour of the fluid changes. The change in behaviour of the fluid also corresponds to a change in the drag force acting on the object.

For a given fluid *(in this case air)* which is interacting with a shape with specific streamlined characteristics, there will be a critical velocity at which the boundary layer will automatically become turbulent. That is, it will no longer flow in a layer like pattern.

In such circumstances, where the air in the boundary layer starts to mix with adjacent layers, there is a tendency for air next to the surface of the ball to follow the outline of the ball more closely before breaking away. A consequence of this is that the area of low pressure at the back of the ball is smaller than it was before the critical velocity was reached, and thus the drag force is reduced: **Figure 6.3.**

Figure 6.3: *Reduction of drag by late separation of air flow around ball travelling above the critical velocity.*

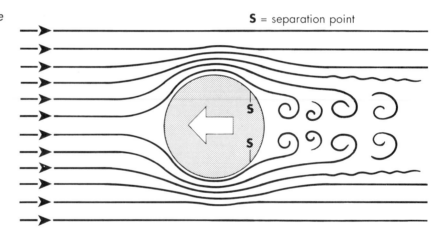

S = separation point

It is important to recognize, that as the object must behave in accordance with Newton's Laws, the observed changes in motion resulting from the fluid forces will vary according to the mass of the object. This is a direct application of Newton's Second Law *(F = m × a)*, so the acceleration arising from the fluid forces will be directly proportional to the object's mass.

In an earlier section it was seen that for objects projected into the air, gravitational force will cause the object to travel in a parabolic flight path. It should be noted that this would only be strictly true if the object was travelling in a vacuum. The flight path of all objects will to some extent be influenced by fluid forces. **Figure 6.4** shows how the path of a projectile may be modified when drag forces are taken into account.

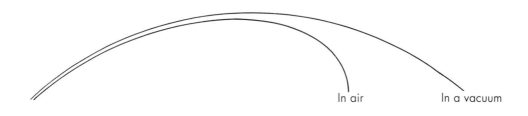

In air   In a vacuum

Figure 6.4: *Projectile flight paths in a vacuum and in air.*

Before considering some additional factors which can give rise to fluid forces, it is worth remembering that it is possible for an object to be experiencing a zero acceleration whilst it is in the air. This of course would arise when the object was experiencing a net zero force.

The best example of this can be seen in sky diving. As the sky diver leaves the plane s/he is accelerated under the effect of gravity. At the same time however, the diver experiences a retarding force acting vertically up on him/her *(air resistance)*. As the sky diver's velocity increases so does the air resistance acting on him/her, up until the point where the retarding force is equal to the gravitational force *(weight of the sky diver)*. At this point the diver experiences zero acceleration and has reached what is termed his/her terminal velocity. The terminal velocity is influenced by the cross sectional area of the diver at right angles to the direction of air flow. If the diver adjusts his/her body shape to decrease the cross sectional area then the terminal velocity will be increased, and vice versa. If the parachute is deployed then the cross sectional area is greatly increased, and the terminal velocity is decreased to a level which allows safe landing.

❖ *Sports Mechanics Applications*

Spring et al (1988) investigated the influence of cross sectional area on the drag experienced by cross country skiers and the corresponding changes in their velocity. The study reported that the drag area of the skiers was reduced by 50% in the squatting position, as compared to the upright position. A reduction of drag area of 30% was reported for skiers wearing competition suits as compared to normal ski suits; and a reduction of drag by 25% when a skier followed close behind another competitor.

Dapena and Feltner (1987) developed a theoretical model to estimate the effects of wind and altitude on 100 m sprint running performance. Their results suggested that a 2 m·s^{-1} tail wind would produce a 0.07 s advantage, whilst a headwind of the same magnitude would increase times by 0.085 s. An advantage of 0.05 s was also suggested for a 100 m race at 2500 m altitude. These values were smaller than previous studies had reported.

The sky diving example serves to emphasise the importance in many sports of reducing the drag forces. Just as the sky diver could alter body shape and alter the drag forces, so speed skiers, downhill skiers, cyclists, bobsleigh competitors, etc., all try to adopt streamlined positions to reduce drag. The degree of streamlining that a sportsperson can get benefit from depends on the body positions that are possible, and/or rules regarding equipment. An ideal streamlined shape has a 'tear drop' profile. A speed skier's helmet displays a profile which comes close to this shape. Also speed skiers insert wedges in between their calves and ski suit which gives their lower leg a 'tear drop' profile: **Figure 6.5**.

Figure 6.5: *Streamlined 'tear drop' profile.*

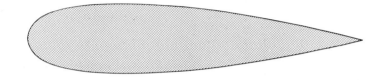

6.2.3 SURFACE CHARACTERISTICS

In section 6.2.1, it was explained that the boundary layer is automatically triggered into turbulence at a critical value, with a consequent reduction in drag, this phenomenum can also be triggered by the surface characteristics of the object. One of the best examples in a sports context, where surface characteristics are important, is the golf ball. The surface of the golf ball is not smooth but is patterned with dimples which vary in shape and size according to manufacturer. The effect of the dimples is to trigger the boundary layer into turbulence thereby reducing drag and allowing the ball to travel further.

This last example serves to emphasise that the characteristics of flow near to the surface of sports objects can be very complex. Efforts to reduce one type of drag may increase another. In sports such as golf, the mixing of air in the layers of air close to the surface of the ball, which results from a 'dimpled' surface, produces a reduction in form drag which is significantly greater than the associated increase in surface drag. It is therefore advantageous to have a 'rough' surface'. In other sports, such as bob sleighing and motor racing, where the surface area is large and the shape is more aerodynamic, the advantage of having a smooth surface is generally more important. This is because the 'shape' will tend to reduce form drag in its own right, so that reducing surface drag becomes much more significant.

A cricket ball has a large seam, which means that the ball is not a regular sphere. Bowlers have exploited this feature of the ball, not only to get the ball to deviate off the pitch when it lands on the seam, but to move or 'swing' it in the air as it approaches the person batting.

In order to achieve the swing, the bowler must be able to bowl the ball in such a manner that the ball travels down the pitch with the seam in a vertical orientation and pointing away from the person batting. In such circumstances the air flowing around the ball will behave differently on different sides of the ball. This is shown in **Figure 6.6**.

The air flowing around the side of the ball which meets the seam early on, is triggered into turbulent flow as described above. As a consequence it tends to 'cling' to the ball's surface and only breaks away towards the rear surface.

The air on the opposite side, which does not meet the seam near the leading surface, breaks away from the surface of the ball much earlier. Because of these different flow patterns, the pressures on opposing sides of the ball are also different, and as a consequence there is a force acting across the ball from the high pressure area to the low. It is this force acting sideways to the direction of travel of the ball which causes it to swing.

By adjusting the seam position to either point towards the leg side, or towards the slip fielders on the off side, the skillful bowler can get the ball to display 'inswing' or 'outswing' respectively.

The use of the seam to trigger different air flows on different sides of the ball may also be produced by making sure that the surface of one side of the ball is smoother than the other. It is for this reason that bowlers are seen rubbing one side of the ball on their trousers whilst walking back for their run up. It is important to note that only one side of the ball should be shined in order to achieve the effect.

One point of interest that arises from the above example, is the notion that if the ball passed the critical velocity identified earlier in this chapter, then the air would be turbulent on both sides of the ball, and therefore the pressure difference would not exist. This may well be the reason why genuinely fast bowlers find it difficult to swing the ball.

The phenomenun of 'late swing' may also be accounted for if the ball is released above the critical value, but on its flight towards the person batting, it slows down below the critical velocity due to form drag. In these circumstances the period of early flight will not facilitate swing, but conditions will be right for swing to occur late in the flight.

Figure 6.6: *View from above of air flow around a cricket ball.*

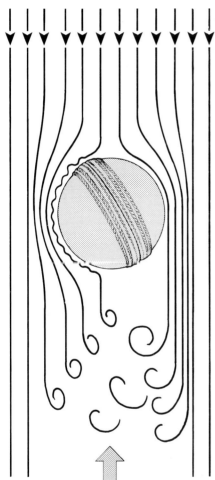

Direction of flight of cricket ball

6.2.4 SPIN

Tennis players hitting ground strokes will frequently apply either top spin or back spin to their shots.

In the situation of top spin, the ball will be rotating forwards as it flies through the air. The general direction of the air flowing past the top of the ball will be opposite to the direction of spin, and therefore because of surface friction, the air next to the surface of the ball will tend to be slowed down.

At the bottom of the ball, the direction of spin is in the **same** direction as the general flow of the ball, and therefore the velocity of the air next to the surface of the ball will not be slowed down as much as that at the top of the ball. The difference in velocities of the air at the top and the bottom of the ball, will, according to the Bernoulli effect, result in a pressure difference. As a consequence of this pressure difference, there will be a force acting which changes the flight path of the ball in a downwards direction. As the force tends to make the ball dip, then the ball can be hit higher over the net *(decreasing the risk of hitting the net)*, and the ball will still land in.

If the tennis player had hit the ball with back spin, then precisely the opposite effect would have occurred. That is, there would have been a vertical component acting upwards on the ball as a result of the spin. The magnitude of this upward force is small compared to the gravitational force experienced by the ball, but it does give the ball a potentially longer period of flight. The advantages that a tennis player might get from back spin are probably more closely associated with the changes in motion experienced by the ball on contact with the surface, than with the flight characteristics. However the additional time the ball is in the air might give the player an opportunity to get to the net.

The effect of changing the pressure distribution on an object because of its spin characteristics is called the **Magnus effect**: Figure 6.7.

Figure 6.7: *The Magnus effect present in a top spin situation.*

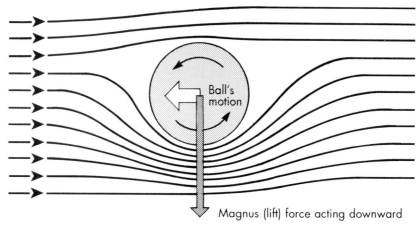

Magnus (lift) force acting downward

In the previous example, the axis of rotation of the body was taken to be one that was at right angles to the direction of flight and parallel to the ground. In reality, the axis might be at some angle to the ground in which case there would be a sideways component of the force, as well as a vertical component.

A number of techniques in sport utilise the Magnus effect to induce a sideways force which can cause the ball to curve. A soccer player trying to bend the ball around 'the wall' of defenders will impart spin to the ball about an axis which ideally will be at right angles to the ground. In this situation the ball will curve in the same direction as the spin. This effect is not always a planned part of sports techniques as is frequently observed in golf, where golfers trying to hit a straight drive may cause their ball to either hook or slice.

The effects described so far have largely been related to situations where sports balls have been interacting with a fluid environment. The principles will also affect all sports implements and performers to either a greater or lesser degree.

One principle which has as yet to be discussed fully but which is important to events such as discus and javelin is the principle of lift.

6.2.5 LIFT

Lift is the term used to describe the force which acts on an object at $90°$ to the direction of travel of the object. It should be remembered that the Magnus effect, described earlier, generated a lift force. In the case of back spin, the direction of the lift force will be in a generally upwards direction. In the case of top spin however, the lift force will be acting in a generally downwards direction. **It is important to note that the term 'lift' does not automatically imply an upwards direction.**

A lift force arises when the air on one side of an object is travelling faster than the air on the opposite side, and is not only present in spin situations.

The best example of a shape which induces an air flow pattern where air on opposing sides has different velocities *(and different pressures)*, is an aerofoil shape. For a shape as shown in **Figure 5.8** the different flow characteristics will result in an upward acting force being present.

Figure 6.8: *Airflow around an aerofoil shape.*

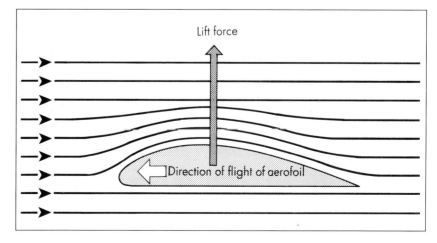

This shape does not frequently occur in sports situations in a pure form *(unless aerobatics or motor racing are included in the definition of sport)*. Nevertheless, the same effect can be achieved for some shapes without a true aerofoil profile. This is brought about by changing the angle at which the object is positioned relative to the flow of air. One of the best events to illustrate this is the discus.

If the midline of the discus is parallel to the direction of flow of air as it flies through the air as shown in **Figure 6.9**, then while it may experience drag forces, the flow on the bottom and top surfaces will have the same characteristics, and therefore there will be no pressure differences between the two surfaces.

Figure 6.9: *Air flow around a discus without an angle of attack.*

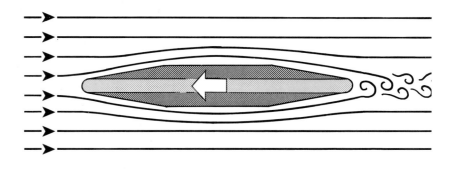

If the discus is positioned so that its midline is at some angle to the main direction of flow *(the angle of attack)*, then the flow around the discus will exhibit the same characteristics as the flow around an aerofoil profile. This means that the velocity on the top surface will be relatively high compared with the velocity on the bottom surface. The force which arises from the pressure differences is called the lift force. As this force has a large component in the vertical direction, which will oppose the gravitational force, it may help to extend the flight phase of the discus.

The magnitude of the lift force can be varied by changing the angle of attack. Increasing the angle of attack up to a certain point may increase the lift force, but there will also be an increase in drag force so an advantage is not always gained . In some events, if the angle of attack is too large the implement being thrown may 'stall' and fall out of the air quite suddenly. This occurs quite often in javelin competitions, where the javelin has been released at too steep an angle.

6.3 INTERACTIONS IN A WATER ENVIRONMENT

It was stated at the start of this chapter that interactions with a water environment would only be dealt with briefly. The complex situation for mixed water/air environments such as that relevant to sailing will not be dealt with, but a brief account of forces associated with swimming will be given. It should therefore be noted that this account only deals with the fluid forces resulting from the swimmer's interaction with water, and not with air.

6.3.1 DRAG AND LIFT

The principles outlined in the previous section, explaining form drag and surface friction, can be directly related to the water environment.

In the case of form drag, the swimmer will need to try and minimize the cross sectional area of the body that is presented to the water. The larger the cross sectional area the larger the drag force. This is easily observed in beginner swimmers, who in an attempt to keep their head out of the water, adopt a poor body position and therefore experience a large drag force. Clearly the form drag force in this situation is of no help to the swimmer. However, in another element of the swimmer's technique, profile/form drag can have positive effects.

In the front crawl technique, the arms are the main form of propulsion. If the arms and hands are pulled straight back underneath the body then there will be a high pressure area on the palm of the hand and a low pressure area on the back of the hand. From the principles discussed in the previous section it will now be clear that there is a force acting from the high pressure area to the low pressure area. As this force is acting in the direction of travel of the swimmer it has a beneficial effect for the swimmer. Profile drag in this context is sometimes called '**propulsive drag**'. This principle is also applicable to other strokes, but cannot completely account for the propulsion gained from the arm action of swimmers.

In the case of surface drag, some swimmers will try to minimise its effects by actually shaving their bodies to try and ensure that the skin surface is as smooth as possible.

In addition to profile and surface drag, the swimmer will also experience a drag force known as **wave drag**. This is essentially the reaction force exerted by the water on the swimmer due to the swimmer exerting a force on the water, and creating waves.

In the example described above for the front crawl, it was assumed that the swimmer generated propulsion from the arm action by pulling the arms straight back underneath the body. In fact swimmers tend to use a 'C' shaped path of pull and to explain this the idea of lift needs to be introduced.

In the previous section, it was seen that by giving an angle of attack to a discus, it could create an air flow which would induce a lift force. A swimmer, by angling the hand and moving it sideways during the pull phase of the arm action, can similarly create a water flow around the hand which induces a lift force. It is this lift force, in combination with the propulsive drag force, that gives the swimmer effective propulsion from the arms. **Figure 6.10** shows part of the path of a swimmer's hand during the pull phase of the front crawl stroke. In the inward and outward phases of the pull the lift force will be acting predominantly in a forwards direction.

Figure 6.10: *The path of the hand in the major pull phase of the front crawl technique.*

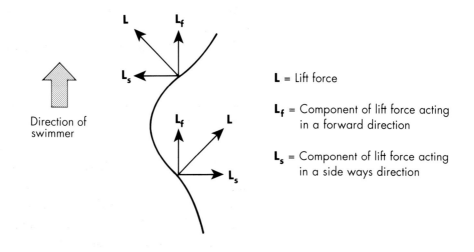

L = Lift force

L_f = Component of lift force acting in a forward direction

L_s = Component of lift force acting in a side ways direction

Direction of swimmer

Similar 'C' shaped pulls are observed in back stroke, and figure of eight and key-hole shaped hand paths are observed in breast stroke and butterfly stroke respectively. These techniques are all making use of the lift force to assist their propulsion.

6.3.2 BUOYANT FORCE

The drag and lift forces are primarily concerned with changing the swimmers horizontal motion, whereas the buoyant force is responsible for keeping the swimmer afloat

The basic principle, is that a swimmer will experience an upward acting buoyant force equal to the weight of the volume of water that has been displaced by his/her body.

The volume, and hence the weight of water displaced by the swimmer, will depend on the constituent matter of the body, that is muscle, bone, fat, etc. Fat has a fairly large volume for a given mass when compared to muscle and other body tissues. Therefore, for two people with the same overall mass, but with different levels of fat and muscle, assuming other factors are equal, the individual with a greater proportion of fat will float more easily.

An improved capacity to float can also be achieved by taking a deep breath. This causes the volume of the lungs to expand but there is only a very small increase in mass, namely the air that has been breathed in.

❖ *Sports Mechanics Application*

In an investigation by Clarys (1978) considering the effects of different body forms on resistive drag, a comparison was made between passive drag and active drag using 44 subjects. passive drag was the recorded resistive force when a swimmer was towed in the prone position with body segments kept still, and active drag was the resistive force recorded when the swimmer used a normal front crawl technique. The investigation found that passive drag did change as a function of body form, where measures of body form included weight, volume, and surface area. However, no correlation was found between active drag and body form. The value of active drag was found to be approximately twice that of passive drag. The study concluded that the form of the human body had little, if any, influence on the resistive drag experienced by a swimmer during normal front crawl swimming. It was suggested that the drag was more dependent on body position and the precise technique of the swimmer.

SUMMARY

In this chapter the reader has been introduced to the following key ideas.

❖ Objects interacting with fluid environments evoke forces and their motion is changed in accordance with Newton's Laws.

❖ The principles associated with pressure/velocity changes in air flows.

❖ The principles affecting drag forces; surface and profile drag.

❖ The Magnus effect.

❖ The principle of lift.

❖ The principle of drag in a water environment; form *(resistive and propulsive)*, surface and wave.

❖ The principle of lift in a water environment.

❖ The principle of the buoyant force.

Sports Mechanics Applications
REFERENCES

Bishop, R. & Hay, J. (1979). The mechanics of hanging in the air. *Medicine and Science in Sports and Exercise*, Vol 11, No 3.

Burden, A. & Bartlett, R. (1989). A kinematic comparison between elite fast bowlers and college fast medium bowlers. *Proceedings of Sports Biomechanics Section of British Association of Sports Sciences.*

Cavanagh, P. R., Andrew, G. C., Kram, R., Rodgers, M. M., Sanderson, D. J., & Hennig, E. M. (1985). An approach to biomechanical profiling of elite distance runners. *International Journal of Sports Biomechanics.*

Clarys, J. P. (1981) Relationship of human body form to passive and active hydrodynamic drag. In A. Morecki, K. Fidelus, K. Kedzior, & A. E. Wit (Eds.), *Biomechanics VIB*. University Park Press.

Dapena, J. (1987). Basic and applied research in the biomechanics of high jumping. In B. Van Gheluwe & J. Atha (Eds.), *Current Research in Sports Biomechanics*. Karger Basel.

Dapena, J. & Feltner M. (1987). Effects of wind and altitude on the times of 100 metre sprint races. *International Journal of Sports Biomechanics*, Vol 3, No 1.

Dyson, G. (1986). *The Mechanics of Athletics* (8th Edition). Hodder and Stoughton.

Hay, J. et al (1986). The techniques of elite male long jumpers. *Journal of Biomechanics*, Vol 9, No 10.

Hay, J. & Reid, J. (1988). *Anatomy, Mechanics and Human Motion* (2nd Edition). Prentice Hall.

Hwang, I. et al (1987). Take off mechanics of double backward somersaults. *International Journal of Sports Biomechanics*, Vol 3, No1.

Kollath, E. & Schwintz, A. (1988). Biomechanical analysis of the soccer throw in. In T Reilly et al (Eds.), *Science and Football*. E. and F. N. Spon.

Lees, A. & Fahmi, E. (1983). Instantaneous power output as measured by a force platform and its relationship to muscular contraction. *Proceedings of Sport and Science Conference*. British Association of Sports Science.

Lees, A. & Aitchison, I. (1983). A Biomechanical analysis of place kicking in rugby. *Proceedings of Sport and Science Conference*. British Association of Sports Science.

McDonald, C. & Dapena, J. (1991). Linear kinematics of the mens 110 m and womens 100 m hurdles race. *Medicine and Science in Sports and Exercise*, Vol 23, No 12.

Miller, D. (1990). Ground reaction forces. In P. R. Cavanagh (Ed.), *Biomechanics of Distance Running*. Human Kinetics.

Sanders, R. & Wilson, D. (1987). Angular momentum requirements of the twisting and non twisting forward one and a half somersault. *International Journal of Sports Biomechanics*, Vol 4, No 2.

Spring, E. et al (1987). Drag area of cross country skiers. *International Journal of Sports Biomechanics*, Vol 4, No 2.

Van Gheluwe, B. & Depot, E. (1992). Friction measurement in tennis on the field and in the laboratory. *International Journal of Sports Biomechanics*, Vol 8, No 1.

Wood, G. (1987). Biomechanical limitations to sprinting speed. In B. Van Gheluwe & J. Atha (Eds.), *Current Research in Sports Biomechanics*. Karger Basel.

BIBLIOGRAPHY

DAISH, C. B. (1972). *The Physics of Ball Skills*. English University Press.

DYSON, G. (revised by Woods, B. & Travers, P.). (1986). *Dyson's Mechanics of Athletics* (Eighth Edition). Hodder and Stoughton.

ENOKA, R. (1994). *Neuromechanical Basis of Kinesiology* (Second Edition). Human Kinetics.

HAY, J. (1978). *The Biomechanics of Sport Techniques* (Second Edition). Prentice Hall.

HAY, J. (1994). *The Biomechanics of Sports Techniques* (Fourth Edition). Prentice Hall.

HAY, J. & REID, J. (1988). *Anatomy and Mechanics of Human Motion*. Prentice Hall.

KREIGBAUM, E. & BARTHELS, K. (1990). *Biomechanics: A Qualitative Approach To Studying Human Movement* (Third Edition). Macmillan.

POLE, S. (1987). *Explaining Physics* (Second Edition). Oxford University Press.

ROWELL, G. & HERBERT, S. (1987). *Physics - a course for GCSE*. Cambridge University Press

SPRUNT, K. (1992). *An Introduction to Sports Mechanics* (Home Learning Pack). National Coaching Foundation.

WATKINS, J. (1983). *An Introduction to Mechanics of Human Movement*. MTP Press

APPENDIX

UNITS OF MEASUREMENT

Description	Unit	Notation
Distance/Displacement	metres	m
Speed/Velocity	metres per second	m/s or m·s^{-1}
Acceleration	metres per second per second	m/s^2 or m·s^{-2}
Inertia/Mass	kilograms	kg
Force	newtons	N
Pressure	newtons per metres squared or pascals	N/m^2 or N·m^{-2} Pa
Momentum	kilograms metres per second	kg m/s or kg·m·s^{-1}
Angular Distance/ Angular Displacement	degrees, radians	° , rad
Angular Velocity	degees per second, radians per second	°/s, rad/s or rad·s^{-1}
Angular Acceleration	degrees per second per second , radians per second per second	°/s^2 , rad/s^2 or rad·s^{-2}
Torque/Moment	newton metres	N·m
Moment of Inertia	kilograms metres squared	kg·m^2
Angular Momentum	kilograms metres squared per second	kg·m^2/s or kg·m^2·s^{-1}
Work	newton metres or joules	N·m or J
Energy	joules	J or kg·m^2/s^2 or N·m
Power	watts	W or J/s or J·s^{-1}

INDEX

A

Acceleration 7
  angular 91
  due to gravity 34
  negative 8
  Newton's second law 31-5
  numerical calculations of 20-1
  positive 8
  segmental 40
Action/reaction
  (Newton's third law) 35
Active drag 124
Aerofoil 119, 120
Angle
  of attack 120
  of release 68, 70
Angular
  acceleration 91
  displacement 86
  distance 86
  impulse 106
  kinetic energy 77
  momentum 102, 103
  motion 91, 110
  position 90, 91
  speed 88
  vectors 85, 86
  velocity 88, 91, 103
Anterior-posterior
  (forward-backward)
  ground reaction force 53
Average
  speed 5
  velocity 5
Axis 94

B

Basketball 74
Bend running 53
Bernoulli effect 112
  boundary layer 113

Boomerang 101
Bowls 59
Buoyant force 123

C

Centre
  of gravity (mass) 40, 70-6
  of pressure 62
Coefficient
  of limiting friction 63
Component vectors 12
  construction technique 13
  numerical calculation 14
Conservation
  of angular momentum 102
  of energy 78
  of linear momentum 59
Contact
  forces 26
  spike in running 58
Cricket ball 5, 65-8, 117
Cross country skiing 115

D

Deceleration 8
Direct method of force
  measurement 60
Direction 6
Discus 120
Displacement 1, 60
Distance 1
  versus Time graph 16
Diving 23, 108
Drag 121
  form/profile 113
  propulsive 122
  surface 113
  wave 123
Dynamic equilibrium 37

E

Eccentric force 93
Eddies 113
Effort force 95
Elasticity 59

Energy 76-83
  angular kinetic 78
  conservation of 78
  gravitational potential 77
  kinetic 77-8
  potential 77
  strain/elastic 77
Equilibrium 38
  dynamic 38
  static 38
External force 26
  torque 102

F

First class lever 95
Flick flack 107
Flotation 123
Flow, laminar 112
Fluid forces 111
Force 25
  action/reaction 36
  and acceleration 31
  and centre of gravity 75
  direct measurement of 60
  drag 124
  effort 95
  external 26
  fluid 111
  friction 62-4
  gravitational 24
  ground reaction 39
  impulse 47
  indirect measurement of 60
  internal 26
  and levers 95
  lift 119
  moments of 94
  and motion relationships 60
  net 37
  normal 64
  off-centre 93
  resistive 95
  and running 52, 56
  and vertical jump 41
  weight 34
Form drag 113
Friction 29, 62
  limiting 62-4
  sliding 62-4
Front crawl 121, 122

G

Golf	86, 87, 116
Gradient	16
Gravitational	
force *(weight)*	42, 71
impulse	4-52, 59.
potential energy	76
Gravity	27
Newton's law of	24
Centre of	70-6
Ground reaction force	39, 42
anterior-posterior *(forward-backward)*	53
horizontal	52
medio-lateral *(side to side)*	53
vertical	56
Gymnastics	98, 101-9

H

'Hang'	74
Height of release	69
High jump	47, 73, 74
Hitch kick	104-5
Horizontal	
ground reaction force	52
velocity	66
Hurdling	70

I

Ice Hockey	29, 36
Impulse	47, 59
acting on runner	53-6
momentum relationship	47
Indirect methods of force	
measurement	60
Inertia	28
inertial value *(reluctance)*	103
Initial impact peak in run	57
Instantaneous speed	5
velocity	5
Internal force	26, 41

J

Javelin	120
Joule	78

K

Kinetic energy	78
angular	78
linear	78

L

Lacrosse	96
Laminar flow	112
Law of conservation of	
energy	78
of gravitation *(Newton's)*	24
of inertia	29
Lay figure	38
Levers	95
first class	95
second class	96
third class	96
Lift	119, 121
Limiting	
friction	62
coefficient of	64
Linear	
kinetic energy	78
momentum	30-5, 59
motion	1, 16, 29
Link model	39
Long jump	15, 28, 70, 104, 105

M

Magnus effect	118
Mass	27
Moment	71, 93-4
arm	94
of inertia	103
Momentum	30-5
angular	102-8
linear	30-5, 59
Motion linear	85

N

Negative	
acceleration	8
velocity	7
work	84

Net	
force	37, 75
impulse	49-52
external torque	102
torque	94
Newton's	
first law of motion *(linear)*	28, 37
first law of motion *(angular)*	102
second law of motion *(linear)*	30-5
second law of motion *(angular)*	106
third law of motion *(linear)*	35-6, 53, 59
third law of motion *(angular)*	108
law of gravitation	27, 70
Non	
contact forces	26
support situations	101
Normal force	63, 64

O

Off-centre force	93
Optimum angle of release	68
Orthogonal components of a ground reaction force	52

P

Parabolic flight path	66, 114
Parallelogram method	11, 32
Passive drag	124
Position	1
of centre of gravity	71
Positive acceleration	8
velocity	6
work	84
Potential energy	77
gravitational	77
strain/elastic	77
Power	80, 82
output	80

Pressure   61
   centre of   62
   gradient   113
Profile drag   113
Projectiles   65
   principles   72
   range   68
Propulsive drag   121
Pythagoras's theorem   12

Q

R

Range   67, 68
Reference level   77
Relative height of release   70
Reluctance to change   28
Resistive force   95
Resultant   10
   vectors   11, 32-4
   construction techniques   11
   momentum   33
   numerical calculations   12
Right hand rule   85
Rotation generation   98
Rowing   95
Rugby   65, 92
Running   3, 9, 89-91
Running shoes   58, 63, 64

S

Scalar quantities   3, 10
Scissors high jump   73
Second class lever   96
Segmental
   acceleration   40
   rotation   99
Shuttle run   6
Skiing   63, 115
Sky diving   115
Sliding friction   64
Slope   16
Soccer   32, 88

Speed   3
   average   5
   instantaneous   6
   of release   69
   versus time graph   14
Spin   118
Sport shoe design   58, 63, 64
Sprint running   9, 30, 53, 56,
                         105, 115, 116
Spring board diving   23
Stability   75
Stall   120
Static equilibrium   37
Strain/elastic energy   77
Stream lines   112
Sumo wrestling   76
Surface drag   113
Swimming   121, 122

T

Tangent   18
Tennis   65
   serve   79, 80
   spin   118
'Tear drop' profile   116
Terminal velocity in sky diving
                                   115
Third class lever   96
Throw-ins   88
Torque   93-4, 108
Trampoline   102, 109
Treadmill running   89-91
Triathlon   2, 4
Turbulent flow   113
Turning moment   71

U

Units of measurement   128

V

Vectors   3, 10
   angular   85-8
   characteristics   10
   components   12
   resultant   11

Velocity   3
   angular   88
   average   5
   components   23, 66
   instantaneous   5
   of release   69
   terminal   115
   vectors   10
Vertical
   ground reaction force in
      running.   56-7
     jumps   21, 41-6, 48-9, 82
   velocity   51
Volleyball block   80

W

Water environment   121
Wave drag   122
Weight   27, 34, 42, 115
   training   96
Work   76, 82
   done   80
   negative   82
   positive   82
Wrestling Sumo   76

X

Y

Z

Zero
   momentum   44
   velocity   44, 51